Practical Wire Antennas 2

Edited by

Ian Poole, G3YWX

Published by the
Radio Society of Great Britain,
Lambda House, Cranborne Road, Potters Bar, Herts. EN6 3JE, UK

1st Edition 2005

Reprinted 2006, 2008

ISBN 9781-9050-8604-7

Cover design: Jodie Escott, M3TPQ
Subediting: Steve Telenius-Lowe, G4JVG
Typography: Chris Danby, G0DWV
Production: Mark Allgar, M1MPA

Printed in Great Britain by Latimer Trend of Plymouth

Contents

Preface

This book has been largely based around the very popular classic work by John Heys, G3BDQ, entitled *Practical Wire Antennas* and published by the RSGB in 1986. *Practical Wire Antennas* has been out of print since 2000 and instead of simply reprinting it, the opportunity has now been taken to edit, update and add further material. Thanks are due to John for all the work he put into the original book and the generous advice he gave in making suggestions for this work. In addition, material has been drawn from a number of sources including the *RSGB Radio Communications Handbook, HF Antennas for All Locations* by Les Moxon, G6XN, and articles that have appeared in *RadCom*. These are credited individually in the text. Thanks are due to all the authors for their contributions, initially for developing the antennas, and later writing about them.

It is often said that the most important part of any radio station is its antenna. It may be difficult to justify claims of this nature because each part of a radio station has its part to play, and without either a transmitter, receiver, or an antenna, the whole station would not operate. However, it is true to say that the efficiency of the antenna will enable the rest of the station to perform to its best. A poor antenna will mean that even the best equipment will perform in a mediocre manner, while a good antenna will allow a station with low power to make some very interesting contacts.

With this in mind, time and effort invested in improving the antenna system is very well spent. Yet this does not necessarily mean spending a large amount of money on an elegant beam antenna atop a tall tower. While many aspire to this type of scenario, often the reality is that this is a dream that cannot be achieved as space and other limitations often prevent the installation of such a system. However, this does not mean that an effective antenna cannot be installed. Many wire antennas are able to perform very well and they do not have the same visual impact as towers and tubular beams.

In addition to this, it is easier to build and experiment with wire antennas. It is hoped that this collection of antenna designs and ideas will help people to capture the enjoyment of experimenting in the true spirit of amateur radio, improving their stations, and being able to say that they have constructed an important part of it. If this is the case, the book will have succeeded in its aim.

It should always be remembered that safety is of prime importance. With the growing awareness of the hazards of exposure to RF, levels of RF should always be kept to an absolute minimum. Some of the antennas described were originally used when safety requirements were less rigorous than they are today. It should be remembered that some of the techniques that might have originally been used around living areas should not be applied in the ways in which they used to be, although they can still be used when kept away from inhabited areas.

Ian Poole, G3YWX, January 2005.

Foreword

I feel very privileged to have been given a pre-publication peep at the contents of *Practical Wire Antennas 2*. It is now 16 years since the RSGB published my original book and much has progressed in the amateur radio world since then. Equipment, especially transceivers, has become increasingly complex in design and construction and very few amateur radio operators feel able or competent to construct their own gear. They can, however, for little outlay still build and use any of a wide variety of wire antennas. This new book will I am sure be a success for its 176 pages present the information needed to assemble, erect, test and put into use of any of the numerous antenna designs presented quickly, without having first to plough through mathematical formulae and equations. My own small library of antenna books holds many that outline antenna types and designs but fail to give the 'nitty gritty' details needed to make satisfactory working and effective antennas.

This new and very practical book holds the complete, easy to understand recipes for a wide range of wire antennas. Some will fit small urban gardens and others are best deployed by those lucky enough enough to have plenty of available space in open surroundings. All kinds of situations are catered for in this book. There is a wealth of information and 'know how' on the mechanics of antenna building to be found in Chapter 9 which is headed 'Practical Aspects' and has 14 pages crammed with information on such topics as safety, rope, plastics, pulleys, wire, guys and halyards.

The first *Practical Wire Antennas* ran to several printings and I feel sure that this latest publication, which has been so ably edited and put together by Ian Poole, G3YWX, will prove to become the antenna experimenter's *vade mecum* for many years to come.

John D Heys, G3BDQ, January 2005

Chapter 1
Antenna Basics

Antennas are electric circuits and follow the rules of normal electric circuits, but they have one major difference and that is that they are designed to radiate as much energy as possible as electromagnetic waves to travel over great distances. It is this property that makes them different to other circuits.

In view of this difference, antennas are often treated in slightly different ways to more normal electrical circuits. It also makes them very interesting to study and use. In the HF portion of the spectrum, antennas can be relatively large, with their dimensions extending to many metres, making them ideal for experimentation.

To be able to gain successful results it is first necessary to have a basic understanding of the fundamental aspects of antennas. Fortunately a deep mathematical understanding is not required and mathematics will be kept to a minimum in the following chapters. Instead, an overview of the concepts is given here as a useful basis.

RADIATION
The aim of any antenna is to convert the electrical energy supplied to it into an electromagnetic wave that is launched into the ether, and in the opposite direction to take electromagnetic waves that impinge on the antenna and convert them into electrical energy that can be transferred to the receiver.

The actual physics of the radiation of energy from the wire is involved, using Maxwell's equations and differential calculus, and accordingly it is best left to theoretical textbooks. It is sufficient to say here that the current flowing up and down the wire gives rise to a magnetic field around the wire, while the charges in motion (which constitute the current) carry with them an electric field. Due to the reversing nature of the current, the two fields are mutually supporting and expand outwards from the wire, carrying with them energy from the exciting current. There exists in the immediate vicinity of the wire an oscillating field known as the induction field (similar to that surrounding an induction coil or a magnet), but this decays in strength rapidly as the distance from the wire increases. At a distance of $\lambda / 2\pi$, or approximately one-sixth of a wavelength, it is equal in strength to the radiation field but beyond one or two wavelengths has fallen to a negligible level.

Radiation takes place from any elevated wire carrying a radio frequency current unless prevented by screening or cancelled by an opposing field of equal magnitude. At any given frequency and for a given direction relative to the wire the field strength produced at a distant point is proportional to the current multiplied by the length of wire, as it appears to the observer, through which it flows.

RESONANCE

An antenna is a circuit that has capacitance, inductance and resistance. This means that its impedance is frequency dependent and the antenna is a tuned circuit that resonates. Most antennas are operated at or near resonance although this is not always the case.

The resonant frequency of a length of wire is dependent upon its length. The shortest length that resonates at a given frequency is one that is just long enough for an electric charge to travel from one end to the other and back again in the time of one cycle of the energy exciting the antenna. As the charge travels the wire twice, ie to one end and back again, the length of wire needed to permit this is a half-wavelength.

Taking the velocity of an electromagnetic wave to be 299,800,000 metres per second, it is possible to calculate that the wavelength of a signal in free space is:

$$\text{Length (metres)} = \frac{149.9}{\text{Frequency (MHz)}}$$

The actual length of a half-wave antenna is not exactly the same as a half-wavelength of a signal travelling in free space. There are several effects that change this somewhat, making the actual length of a half-wavelength antenna shorter than the free space half-wavelength. The first is that insulators with a different dielectric constant to air are often required at the end of an antenna for support. Other nearby objects may also have a similar effect. However, the main effect depends on the ratio of the wire length to its diameter. The thicker the wire in relation to the wavelength, the shorter the antenna. A factor known as the K factor is the figure by which the free space half-wavelength must be multiplied to give the length for a half-wave antenna. A curve of the K factor is shown in **Fig 1.1**. At HF where wires are used, the K factor may be around 0.98, and this means that an antenna for a frequency that has a free space half-wavelength of 10 metres would need to be 9.8 metres long.

In practice it is always good practice to cut an antenna slightly longer than required, and then once it has been installed to trim its length to give the optimum performance. It is far easier

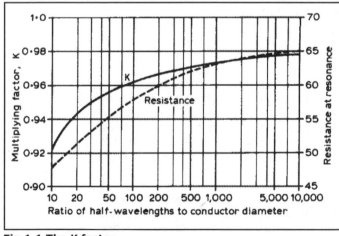

Fig 1.1 The K factor.

to remove wire by cutting it than to have to replace wire when it has been cut too short. It is also a fact that despite all the calculations, spurious effects sometimes mean that lengths are not quite what they are anticipated to be, especially when antennas are mounted in real situations where they may pass close to other objects that may detuned them or where they may have to be bent to fit into the available space.

CURRENT AND VOLTAGE DISTRIBUTION

It has already been mentioned that a charge travels along an antenna wire when it is excited by a signal. If the wire antenna were infinitely long, the charge (voltage) and the current (the electric charge in motion) would both steadily decrease in amplitude with the distance from the source. This would result from the fact that energy is dissipated in the form of radiated energy as well as there being some heat dissipated as a result of the resistance in the antenna wire.

When the antenna has a finite length, charge is reflected when it reaches the far end of the antenna. As the energy is being continually supplied in the form of a sine wave of the signal in question, this can be considered as a series of charges of different amplitude being supplied.

When a half-wavelength antenna is excited with a signal, there is not just a single charge, but a continuous supply of energy, varying in voltage according to a sine wave cycle. It is possible to consider this as a series of charges, all with slightly different amplitudes. When a charge reaches the end of the antenna and is reflected, the direction of current flow is reversed. As there is a continuous supply of charges, the forward and reflected currents add together. At the point of reflection, the charge moving towards the end and the one that has just been reflected are virtually the same. As they are flowing in opposite directions they cancel each other out and no current flows at the end of the antenna.

Away from the end of the antenna, the magnitudes of the outgoing and returning currents differ from each other. This is because the charges have been supplied at different parts of the RF cycle, and the returning charge takes a different time to reach the end of the antenna and be reflected back than the charge that is travelling towards the end. As both charges at a given point have a different magnitude, they do not completely cancel out and a measurable current exists. The greatest difference, ie the largest resultant current, exists at a distance of a quarter-wavelength from the end of the wire. Back still farther from this point the current decreases until, a half-wavelength away from the end of the antenna, it reaches zero again. Thus, in a half-wavelength antenna, the

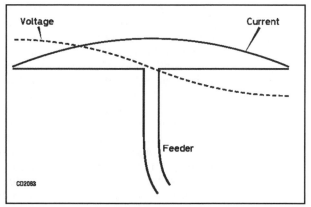

Fig 1.2 Current and voltage waveforms along a half-wavelength dipole.

current is zero at the ends and maximum at the centre, as shown in **Fig1.2**.

The voltage along the wire behaves in a different manner to the current. It reaches its greatest amplitude at the end because, at this point, two practically equal charges add together. Back along the wire, however, the outgoing and returning charges are not equal and their sum is smaller. At a point a quarter-wavelength from the end, the returning charge is equal in magnitude but opposite in phase with the outgoing charge. This is because at this time the polarity of the voltage wave from the source has reversed. The two voltages therefore cancel each other and the resultant voltage is zero. Beyond the quarter-wavelength point, the voltage again increases, but this time with the opposite polarity.

From this it can be seen that the voltage is at its maximum at every point when the current is at its minimum, and vice versa.

DIRECTIVITY

The radiation field which surrounds the wire is not uniformly strong in all directions. It is strongest in directions at right angles to the current flow in the wire and falls in intensity to zero along the axis of the wire. In other words, the wire exhibits *directivity* in its radiation pattern, the energy being concentrated in some directions at the expense of others.

One of the methods of increasing the directivity is to use further wires in the antenna, along with phasing techniques so that signals in some directions are reinforced, whereas in others the signals from the various wires cancel. These antenna arrays are often called *beams* because they concentrate radiation in the desired direction like a beam of light from a torch. Because a number of wires or elements are needed to create this directivity, beam antennas usually require more space than simple ones, and this limits the extent to which they can usefully be employed at the longer wavelengths. As a result of the added complexity and space required, few beam antennas are described in this book.

DIPOLES

One of the most commonly used words in antenna work is *dipole*. A dipole is simply some device (in the present context an antenna) which has two 'poles' or terminals into which radiation-producing currents flow. The two poles may be of any length, and a certain amount of confusion sometimes arises from the failure to state the length involved. In practice it is usually safe to assume that when the word 'dipole' is used by itself, it is intended to describe a half-wavelength antenna, ie a radiator of electrical half-wavelength fed by a balanced connection at the centre. Any reference to gain over a dipole is assumed to refer to this half-wavelength dipole. When reference to another form of dipole is intended, it is usual to state the overall length, eg a full-wavelength dipole, short dipole etc. A short dipole is less than half a wavelength long, but needs to be tuned to resonance by the addition of inductance, usually in the centre, or some form of capacitive end-loading as discussed later. Shortening has little effect on the radiation pattern but, if carried too far, leads to poor efficiency and excessively narrow bandwidth.

Loops containing between two-thirds and one-and-a-half wavelengths of wire have radiation patterns very similar to those of half-wave dipoles.

A further reference sometimes encountered is to the *monopole* or *unipole*. This is an unbalanced radiator, fed against an earth plane, and a common example is the ground-plane vertical.

GAIN

If one antenna system can be made to concentrate more radiation in a certain direction than another antenna, for the same total power supplied, then it is said to exhibit *gain* over the second antenna in that direction. In other words, more power would have to be supplied to the reference antenna to give the same radiated signal in the direction under consideration, and hence the better antenna has effectively gained in power over the other. Gain can be expressed either as a ratio of the powers required to be supplied to each antenna to give equal signals at a distant point, or as the ratio of the signals received at that point from the two antennas when they are driven with the same power input. Gain is usually expressed in decibels. Gain is of course closely related to directivity, but an antenna can be directive and yet have a power *loss* as a result of energy dissipated in antenna wires and surrounding objects. This is actually the reason why it is not possible to obtain high gain figures from electrically small antennas.

It is important to note that in specifying gain for an antenna, some reference to direction must be included, because no antenna can exhibit gain simultaneously in all directions relative to another antenna. The distribution of radiated energy from an antenna may be likened to the shape of a balloon filled with incompressible gas, with the antenna at the centre. The amount of gas represents the power fed to the antenna, and the volume of the balloon can only be increased by putting in more gas. The shape of the balloon may be distorted into many different shapes, and elongated greatly in some directions so that the amount of gas squeezed in those directions is increased, but this can only be achieved by reducing the amount of gas in some other part of the balloon: the total volume must remain unaltered. Likewise the antenna can only direct extra energy in some required direction by radiating less in others.

The gain of an antenna is expressed in terms of its performance relative to some agreed standard. This enables any two antennas to be directly compared. For example, if two antennas have a gain 6dB and 4dB respectively, relative to a given standard, the first has a gain of 6 - 4 = 2dB relative to the second.

It is unfortunate that two standards exist side by side and will be encountered in other references to antennas. One standard often used is the theoretical *isotropic radiator*, which radiates equal power in all directions, ie its solid polar diagram is a sphere. This is a strictly non-practical device which cannot be constructed or used, but has the advantage that the comparison is not complicated by the directional properties of the reference antenna.

The other standard is the half-wave dipole which has its own directional pattern. This is a practical antenna which can be built and is therefore a more realistic basis for comparison, but it should be noted that gain expressed relative to a half-wave dipole (*dBd*) means by inference relative to the maximum radiation from the dipole.

Gain relative to an isotropic radiator is designated as *dBi* but beware of a common tendency to quote the gain of an antenna gain without reference to the standard employed. This can lead to a disparity of 2.15dB in claimed results, this being the difference of the two standards employed (the gain of a half-wave dipole relative to the isotropic source). In some cases it is safer to assume the more conservative figure when comparing different antenna performance unless one is sure that the same reference has been used in each case.

Because direction is inevitably associated with a statement of gain, it is usually assumed in the absence of any qualifying statement that the gain quoted for any antenna is its gain in the direction of its own maximum radiation. Where the antenna system can be rotated, as is often the case on 14MHz and higher frequencies, this is not so important, but when the antenna is fixed in position the superiority it exhibits in one direction over another antenna will not hold in other directions, because of the different shapes of the two directivity patterns. Antenna A may have a quoted gain of 6dB over antenna B, but only in the directions which favour the shape of its radiation pattern relative to that of antenna B.

There is an important distinction between transmitting gain and effective receiving gain. In the first case it is required to maximise the power transmitted and in the second case we have to maximise the signal-to-noise ratio, and the two gains will be the same only if there are no power losses and noise is isotropic, ie arriving equally from all directions. In the HF bands, the useful receiver sensitivity is limited by external noise which is usually well above the receiver noise level and, as long as this remains true, signal-to-noise ratio is unaffected by losses in the antenna system. Typically, with a low-noise receiver, antenna losses could reduce the power transmitted by up to 10dB or more before starting to affect the performance adversely when the same antenna is used for reception.

RADIATION RESISTANCE AND ANTENNA IMPEDANCE

When power is delivered from the transmitter into the antenna, some small part will be lost as heat, since the material of which the antenna is made will have a finite resistance, albeit small, and a current flowing in it will dissipate some power. The bulk of the power will usually be radiated and, since power can only be consumed by a resistance, it is convenient to consider the radiated power as dissipated in a fictitious resistance which is called the *radiation resistance* of the antenna.

Using ordinary circuit relations, if a current I is flowing into the radiation resistance R, a power of I^2R watts is being radiated. As depicted in Fig 1.2 the current distribution along a resonant antenna or indeed any standing wave antenna is not uniform but is approximately sinusoidal. It is therefore necessary to specify the point of reference for the current when formulating the value of the radiation resistance, and it is usual to assume the value of current at the anti-node or maximum point. This is known as the current loop, and hence the value of R given by this current is known as the loop radiation resistance: in practice the word 'loop' is omitted but inferred.

A half-wavelength dipole has a radiation resistance of about 73Ω. If it is made of highly conductive material such as copper or aluminium, the loss resistance may be less than 1Ω. The conductor loss is thus relatively small and the antenna provides an efficient coupling between the transmitter and free space. However, it is important to keep the levels of resistance as low as reasonably possible to ensure the optimum efficiency. With the skin effect the actual resistance can be higher than might be expected, and therefore the use of thick wire made of copper enables these losses to be kept as low as possible.

When the antenna is not a resonant length, it behaves like a resistance in series with a positive (inductive) or negative (capacitive) reactance and requires the addition of an equal but opposing reactance to bring it to resonance, so that it may be effectively supplied with power by the transmitter. The combination of resistance and reactance, which would be measured at the antenna terminals with an impedance meter, is referred to in general terms as the antenna *input impedance*. This impedance is only a pure resistance when the antenna is at one of its resonant lengths.

The input impedance of the antenna is related specifically to the input terminals, whereas the radiation resistance is usually related to the current at its loop position. It is possible to feed power into an antenna at any point along its length so that the input impedance and the loop radiation resistance even of a resonant antenna may be very different in value, although in this case both are pure resistances. Only when the feed point of the antenna coincides with the position of the current loop on a single wire will the two be approximately equal. If the feed point occurs at a position of current minimum and voltage maximum, the input impedance will be very high, but the loop radiation resistance remains unaltered. For a given power fed into the antenna, the actual feed point current measured on an RF ammeter will be very low, but because the input impedance is high, the power delivered to the antenna is the same. Such an antenna is described as voltage fed, because the feed point coincides with a point of maximum voltage in the distribution along the antenna. Conversely an antenna fed at a low-impedance point, usually a current maximum, is described as current fed.

RADIATION PATTERNS AND POLAR DIAGRAMS
From the point of view of effective gain it is immaterial whether this comes from horizontal directivity, vertical directivity or both, but the practical usefulness of a fixed array using horizontal collinear elements is restricted by the relatively narrow beamwidth in the horizontal plane. To illustrate the radiation pattern of an antenna, polar diagrams are used in the form of curves, the radius of which in any direction represents the relative strength of signals in that direction.

The radiation from an antenna occurs in three dimensions and therefore the radiation pattern is best represented by the surface of a solid object. A polar diagram is any section of the solid shape, and a large number of sections may be necessary to reduce the antenna radiation pattern to

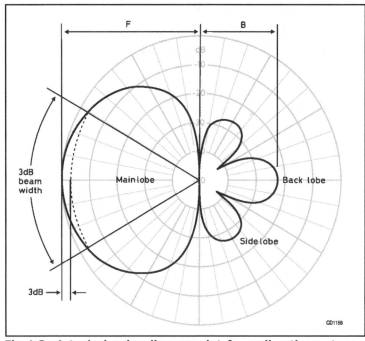

Fig 1.3 A typical polar diagram plot for a directive antenna showing the -3dB points and the beamwidth.

two dimensions. In practice it is necessary to be content with two polar diagrams taken in the principal planes, usually the horizontal and vertical, and giving the two cross-sections of the main beam. Where the polar diagram has a definite directional form, the angle between the directions where the power radiated is half the value at the point of maximum gain (-3dB) is called the beamwidth.

To avoid confusion when discussing radiation, directions in the horizontal plane are referred to as azimuth; angles above the horizontal, in the vertical plane, are called wave angles or directions in elevation. Confusion often arises additionally when the expression horizontal (or vertical) polar diagram is used, unless it is made clear by a statement of the polarisation of the antenna with respect to the earth's surface. When reference is made to the polar diagram of an antenna in free space, the terms 'horizontal' and 'vertical' have no meaning, and the more precise descriptions of E-plane and H-plane polar diagrams are to be preferred. These are unambiguous, since the direction of the electric and magnetic fields around the antenna is a function only of the direction of current flow. The electric field (or E-plane) is parallel to the direction of current and therefore usually parallel to the radiating wire. The magnetic field (or H-plane) is at right angles to the current and therefore normal to the radiating wire. The polar diagram of the half-wave dipole illustrated in **Fig 1.4** is then an E-plane diagram: the H-plane diagram of the dipole would be a circle. Such an antenna is then said to possess E-plane directivity, and is omni-directional in the H-plane.

No matter what name is used to describe the polar diagram, it should be remembered that these radiation patterns are for long distances and cannot be measured accurately at distances less than several wavelengths from the antenna. The greater the gain, the greater the distance required.

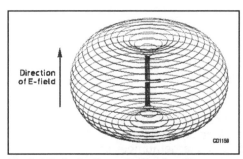

Fig 1.4 Polarisation of a dipole antenna.

In terms of long distance contacts on the HF bands in particular, the angle of elevation (sometimes also called the angle of radiation) of the beam is of importance. The distances that can be achieved are also dependent upon the angles at which the signals travel. From basic trigonometry it can be seen that if a signal leaves the antenna at a low angle of radiation, ie almost parallel to the earth's surface, the distances achieved will be greater than signals leaving with a high angle of radiation, ie travelling at a much

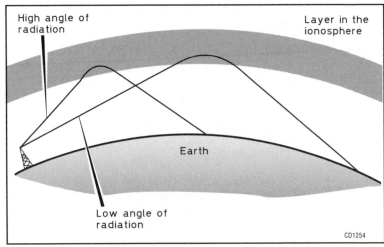

Fig 1.5 Effect of angle of radiation and ionospheric regions on the distances achieved using ionospheric propagation.

steeper angle upwards towards the ionosphere (**Fig 1.5**). Also, the higher the ionospheric region that is used, the greater the distances that will be achieved.

Even relatively small increases in the angle at which the signal leaves the antenna can considerably reduce the distances that can be covered. The maximum distance that can be achieved using the E layer of the ionosphere is generally considered to be 2000km (1250 miles), but this is reduced to just 400km (250 miles) if the angle is 20 degrees. Similarly the maximum distance achievable using the F2 layer reduces from around 4000km (2500 miles) to just under 1000km (600 miles). In view of these figures, most installations where long-haul contacts are required will want to have antennas that produce low-angle radiation.

BANDWIDTH AND Q
There are no unique definitions for antenna bandwidth. Essentially the definition of the bandwidth of an antenna is the band of frequencies over which it will operate satisfactorily. Dependent upon the operational requirements of the antenna, the definitions fall into two categories: impedance bandwidth and the radiation pattern bandwidth.

Impedance bandwidth
It is more usually the impedance bandwidth that limits the operation of amateur HF antennas and it is defined as the frequency range over which the antenna impedance results in a voltage standing wave ratio (VSWR) less than some arbitrary limit. This may be typically 2:1 for amateur operation with solid-state transmitters, or higher values for other applications. Ideally, an antenna should be impedance matched to the feed line and thence to the transmitter or receiver, although this is not the case where tuned feed line antennas are used. Under these circumstances an antenna tuning and matching unit will need to be able

to accommodate the high voltages that are encountered under some circumstances.

Radiation pattern bandwidth

Antenna radiation patterns are dependent upon the operating frequency and under some circumstances they may be of importance. Their sensitivity to frequency changes are in turn dependent on the degree of tuning or inherent Q required to achieve the desired characteristic. Bandwidth is defined as the frequency range over which satisfactory performance can be obtained. The criteria for defining bandwidth could be one or more of the following:

♦ Main lobe beamwidth
♦ Acceptable side lobe level
♦ Minimum gain or directivity
♦ Polarisation qualities

It should be noted that the impedance bandwidth and radiation pattern bandwidth are independent of each other. It is quite possible for the impedance bandwidth to be greater than the radiation pattern bandwidth, especially with high-gain antennas, and to be able to feed power into an antenna that is then wasted by radiating it in other than the desired direction.

POLARISATION

The polarisation of an antenna is defined in terms of the orientation of the electric field vector in the direction of maximum radiation. The maximum radiation from a dipole occurs in a plane bisecting its centre and at right-angles to the dipole axis. The electric field vector in this plane lies parallel to the axis of the dipole. Thus a dipole mounted horizontally above the ground is said to radiate horizontally polarised signals, and the same dipole mounted vertically would radiate vertically polarised signals.

Radio waves comprise both electric and magnetic fields mutually coupled at right-angles to each other and at right-angles to the direction of propagation. The two principal planes used in describing radiation patterns are the E-plane, which lies parallel to the electric vector or E-field in the main lobe, and the H-plane, which lies parallel to the magnetic vector or H-field in the main lobe.

While vertical or horizontal linear polarisation is almost always used for terrestrial communications, circular polarisation may be used in some applications, often at VHF and above and for applications such as satellite communications where it is able to help to reduce the effects of propagation, ground reflections or the spinning motions of the satellites on the signals. The effect of circular polarisation can be visualised as a signal that would be radiated from a dipole that is spinning about its centre at the radiating frequency. The tip of the electric vector traces out a corkscrew as it propagates away from the antenna and, like a corkscrew, the polarisation is described as right or left-handed circular, dependent on the direction of rotation of the electric vector as seen from the transmitter.

For communication in free space, both transmitting and receiving antennas should have the same polarisation for the maximum signal to be received. Any cross polarisation will result in a degradation of the signal proportional to the cosine of the angle between them. Thus at ninety degrees, ie when the antennas are said to be cross-polarised, no signal should be received. In practice there are many reflections, even over short terrestrial paths, and some signal will be received. For ionospheric propagation for most purposes the signal can be thought of as being randomly polarised and cross-polarisation of antennas is not an issue.

There are, however, some advantages for choosing an antenna of a particular polarisation under some circumstances. For ground or surface wave propagation there are major benefits for using vertical polarisation, as signals may be tens of decibels higher using a vertically-polarised antenna than one that is horizontally polarised. It is for this reason that medium-wave broadcast stations that use ground-wave propagation use vertically-polarised antennas. This means that for local topband (160m band) contacts, a loaded vertical antenna is likely to give better results than a larger horizontal one.

ANTENNA WIRE CONSIDERATIONS
The type of wire used in antenna systems can be an important consideration. Any outdoor antenna will be subject to the action of the wind and will swing about for much of the time. Unless sensible precautions are taken when constructing it, metal fatigue will take its inevitable toll.

Multi-strand, plastic-covered wire is cheap and easily found on the surplus market, and there is a temptation to use this kind of wire for most antenna work. However, when used these wires will have a useful life that may not be longer than a few years. The constant movement of the antenna results in the breaking of the conductors, leaving the plastic covering undamaged. When this happens the actual break is difficult to locate and repair. This type of wire often stretches by a considerable degree and the resonant point of the antenna therefore can change.

Single-strand, hard-drawn copper wire of 18 or 16SWG is much better for antenna work, including particularly the fabrication of open-wire lines. It may seem to be more expensive as an initial outlay, but these wires will last for many years. There are some lengths of copper wire 'resting' in the author's wire box which have been part of a variety of antennas during the past 30 years.

Similarly, it must be mentioned that 75Ω twin feed is particularly prone to internal breaks if it is allowed to swing freely.

ANTENNA RECIPROCITY
One of the key features of an antenna is that it can be used both for transmitting and receiving. When being used to receive signals, electromagnetic waves are picked up and converted into electrical signals that are passed down the feeder and presented to the front end of the receiver. In the reverse mode when power is applied to the feeder from a transmitter it passes along the feeder and enters the radiating element of the antenna. Here the electrical signals are converted into electromagnetic

energy that is radiated as a signal. In each case the process is the exact reversal of the other. This means that for all practical purposes the properties of an antenna used for reception are the same as its properties used for transmission. It has the same directive pattern, impedance, efficiency, and so forth. This means that for transmitting the direction where most power is delivered is also the same direction in which the antenna has optimum 'sensitivity'. A poorly-matched antenna with a high level of VSWR on transmit will also present a poor match when used to receive.

This fact can be useful when designing antennas, because some tests are easier to make, or more accurate, when transmitting for example. In this way the test can be performed in the optimum manner, knowing the results hold for both transmitting and receiving.

Obviously parameters such as the power handling limit only apply to the antenna when it is used for transmitting as very high powers are most unlikely to be encountered when receiving.

TYPES OF ANTENNA
There are many ways in which antennas can be categorised. Many references are made to antennas such as *Hertzian* and *Marconi* antennas. The basic Hertz antenna is a half-wavelength long at the operating frequency and is insulated from ground. It is often called a dipole or a doublet. The basic Marconi antenna is a quarter-wavelength long and is either grounded at one end or connected to a network of wires such as a ground plane or a counterpoise. The ground or counterpoise provides the equivalent of an additional quarter-wavelength which is required for the antenna to resonate. Although there are many different interpretations, this gives a useful starting point to look at many different types of antenna.

Antennas may also be categorised according to whether they are *balanced* or *unbalanced*. Essentially a balanced antenna is one such as a dipole where there are two poles or connections to the antenna itself. An unbalanced antenna is where one of the connections of the antenna is an earth or simulated earth in the form of a counterpoise or ground plane. In order to feed an antenna, a balanced or unbalanced feeder is required, as discussed in the next chapter. However, when feeding a dipole or balanced antenna with an unbalanced feeder such as coaxial cable, a *balun* (*bal*anced-to-*un*balanced transformer) is often used to accommodate the change. Further information about baluns is given in Chapter 8, Antenna Matching Systems.

Another popular form of antenna is the end-fed wire. Although these antennas offer many advantages and are described later, one of their disadvantages is that the whole length of the wire radiates. Typically there is no feeder as the antenna starts immediately it leaves the Antenna Tuning Unit (ATU). As this is often located in the vicinity of the radio equipment, ie in the shack, it means that there are likely to be high levels of RF in the shack. Not only can this give rise to difficulties with RF getting back into the equipment, particularly on audio leads, causing feedback and distortion on the audio, but also there may be health hazards associated with high levels of RF. Accordingly these antennas are best used only for receiving, for low power transmitting, or where the antenna can be kept away from any occupied areas by having a remote ATU. Further information about RF exposure levels and safety can be found in a variety of publications including the *ARRL Antenna Book*.

GROUND SYSTEMS

Unbalanced antennas require a ground system for successful operation: the success or failure of the antenna system depends upon the efficiency of the earth system. In turn this is highly dependent upon the conductivity of the ground in the vicinity of the antenna. Moist land provides the best conditions, and indeed a salt marsh would be ideal. Often the underlying rock plays an important part in any ground system, so those who are living on sandstone areas will find difficulty in creating an efficient earth system. Those in more moist areas will generally find it much easier to create a good earth connection.

An earth system can have several constituents. Ground rods, radials, counterpoises; all can form part of the earth system. Not only is a good DC connection required, but a good RF one is also needed. By combining different techniques it is often possible to make a very efficient earth system.

A good DC connection is made by having a conductor in contact with the earth. As the earth has a very low conductivity it is necessary to have as much surface area in contact as possible. The importance of this is illustrated by the fact that even a good DC ground may have a resistance of several ohms and this will considerably reduce the efficiency of the antenna.

To make a DC connection to ground a variety of methods can be used. Ground rods are manufactured for electrical installations. These are typically rods with a steel centre to allow them to be driven into the ground, but with a copper surface. A clamp is then used to make a connection to the wire. These are often quite thin, and they do not present a large surface area to the ground. As a result several may be required. As an alternative, or in addition, discarded lengths of copper water pipe may be buried. As copper is soft, this normally has to be buried as if driven into the ground with a hammer it is likely to buckle and bend. If the separate earth spikes and pipes are spread out, the effect of the low conductivity of the earth itself can be reduced. A typical installation may consist of several rods and pipes connected together using copper braid to ensure a low resistance for the interconnecting wire.

Another approach that is particularly applicable when moving into a new house, or when landscaping a garden, is to bury galvanised chicken wire. This mesh comes in rolls and can be placed under a layer of earth, covered over and then a lawn can be planted over the top. By laying it under a lawn it is less likely to be disturbed. By covering a large area, as well as having a relatively large contact surface area, this method is able to provide a very efficient earth system.

Another interesting idea was set out by John Ellerton, G3NCN, is for the earth system for his 'Skymiser' antenna described in the June 1999 issue of *RadCom*. In this he used a number of 1.3m (4ft) tubular posts. These were driven into the ground a few inches at a time, and then extracted so that the earth that collected in the centre could be removed. This was repeated every few inches until the pipe was almost buried, and this effectively drilled a 2in hole into the ground. Before finally inserting the post into the hole it was drilled transversely with 6mm (0.25in) holes at regular intervals below the expected ground level. The purpose of this was that water poured down the hollow interior of the pipes would moisten the earth around them, thereby keeping the ground moist even during the dry summer months.

Another idea for drilling a hole for an earth rod was developed by John Hey, G3TDZ, and appeared in the December 1980 issue of *RadCom*, see **Fig 1.6**. Having found it difficult to dig a hole about 1.5m deep for a ground without excavating what he describes as a "crater", he used a length of discarded 10cm (4in) plastic pipe that had been discarded. Teeth were cut into the end and these were reinforced with steel cutting edges so that it could be used a bit like an oil drill. A tommy bar made from a length of 13mm (0.5in) aluminium antenna rod, or other suitable rod, is pushed though holes easily made at the upper end. It is then best to use a spade and to dig a small hole about one spade depth to test the surface and clear away the surface rubbish. Then, when drilling starts, liberal doses of water can be used. This not only softens the ground, but also helps to lubricate the drill. Once the hole has been drilled, the ground shaft can be inserted in the new hole, which can then be tightly packed with earth to ensure good contact. Finally the surface can be tidied and returned to its normal state, without the major disruption of digging a large hole.

A variety of approaches may be used from conductive ground rods and other conductive sheets to improve the DC connection to earth, to the use of radials of either insulated or bare copper wire to provide an RF earth with a low impedance. These radials can either be laid on the ground, or buried beneath it. In most cases the option of burying them is preferable because it means they do not then present a trip hazard. Burying radial wires can be easily achieved, even in a lawn, by simply making a narrow slit in the earth with a spade and then dropping the wire into the slit and replacing the earth. Although this will leave a mark in a lawn for a short while, it will soon grow over and will not be visible.

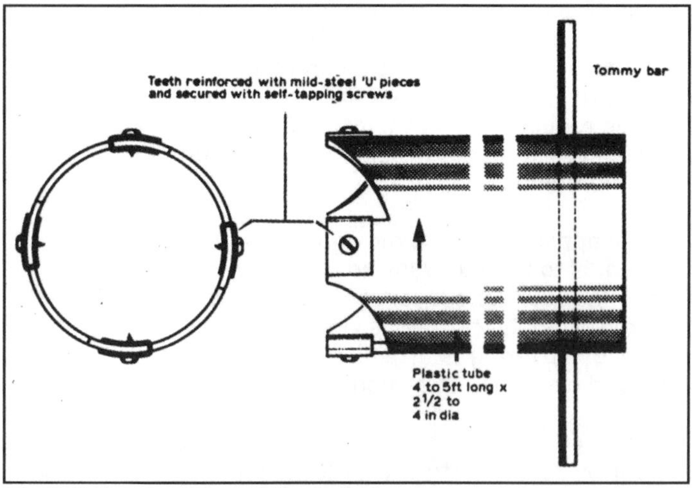

For broadcast stations with few limitations grounding systems may be particularly elaborate, and this has been recognised for many years.

Fig 1.6 Construction of the hole borer.

A report from the 1930s which is still relevant today suggested that a minimum of 120 radials be used, radiating out from the base of the antenna. These radials, it suggested, should be at least half a wavelength long. This number of radials is obviously not viable for most amateur situations and it has been suggested that at least 15 radials is a good compromise. However, even with this number of radials the earth impedance is such that the efficiency of a quarter-wavelength antenna system might fall to around 50% under average conditions.

Another option is to use a counterpoise system. It has been suggested that this is likely to be more efficient than an earth. A counterpoise consists of a number of radials or a grid network of wires elevated above the earth and insulated from it. A 'ground plane' consisting of radials around a vertical antenna is a form of counterpoise.

Chapter 2
Feeders and Connectors

Although not part of the radiating antenna itself, the *feeder*, or feed line, is an integral part of the whole antenna system and its operation governs many of the parameters of the overall antenna system. In fact, there are three separate parts to an antenna system: the radiator, the feeder or feed line between transmitter and radiator, and the coupling arrangements to the transmitter. Wherever possible, the antenna itself should be placed in the best position where it can radiate the optimum signal. As these positions are generally high up and not in the optimum position for the station, it is necessary to have a feed line or feeder to connect the antenna to the transmitter or receiver with a minimum of loss due to resistance or radiation.

By the use of transmission lines or feeders, the power of the transmitter can be carried appreciable distances without much loss due to conductor resistance, insulator losses or radiation. It is thus possible to place the antenna in an advantageous position without having to suffer the effects of radiation from the connecting wires. For example, a 14MHz dipole 10m (32ft) in length can be raised 20m (60ft) high and fed with power without incurring appreciable loss. If, on the other hand, the antenna wire itself were brought down from this height to a transmitter at ground level, most of the radiation would be propagated from the down lead in a high angle direction. An arrangement of this nature would be relatively poor for long-distance communication.

OPERATION OF FEEDERS
A feeder is a transmission line along which power is transferred as an electromagnetic wave. It travels along the transmission line in fundamentally the same as the free-space wave although it is confined to the conductors and the field is curved about the conductors instead of being linear. In one form of feeder in the form of a concentric line (coaxial cable) the current passes along the centre conductor and returns along the inside of the sheath. Due to the so-called *skin effect*, at high frequencies the currents do not penetrate more than a few thousandths of an inch into the metal, and this means there should be no current on the outside of the outer conductor. The fields are thus held inside the cable and there is no radiation, provided that current is not allowed to flow on the outside of the cable.

Another form of feeder using twin lines, the two wires carry 'forward and return' currents producing equal and opposite fields which effectively neutralise each other away from the immediate vicinity of the wires. When the spacing between wires is a very small fraction of the wavelength, the radiation is negligible provided the line is accurately balanced. This means that, in the HF range, a separation of several centimetres may be employed, but in the VHF range a much smaller spacing is required.

CHARACTERISTIC IMPEDANCE

One of the major features of a feeder is its *characteristic impedance*. This is expressed in ohms and just as an antenna has a value of impedance, and a receiver or transmitter has an input or output impedance, so does a feeder. This impedance is very important because it is necessary to match the feeder impedance to that of the rest of the system.

The impedance of the feeder is governed by a number of factors. The physical dimensions of the feeder have a very large bearing. Also, the dielectric constant of the material between and sometimes around the feeder can vary the impedance. These factors are easy to control and therefore all feeders are manufactured or constructed to provide a particular characteristic impedance. A match of the impedance of the receiver and / or transmitter to the feeder, and also the feeder to the antenna, is required to enable the optimum power transfer to take place, and it is for this reason that the impedance of the feeder is important. Where there is a discontinuity or change in impedance, power is reflected and standing waves are set up.

The way in which the characteristic impedance can be visualised is by looking at a travelling wave that is travelling in a certain direction without suffering any reflection or discontinuity. The same applies to transmission lines, although in this case the presence of reflections and therefore standing waves does not cause radiation if the line remains balanced or shielded. If the line were infinitely long and free from losses a signal applied to the input end would travel on for ever, energy being drawn away from the source of signal just as if a resistance had been connected instead of the infinite line. In both cases there is no storage of energy such as there would be if the load included inductance or capacitance and the line, so far as concerns the generator of the signal, is strictly equivalent to a pure resistance. This resistance is known as the characteristic impedance of the line and usually denoted by the symbol Z_0. Suppose now that at some distance from the source we cut the line; what has been removed is still an infinitely long line and equivalent to a resistance Z_0 so if we replace it by an actual resistance of this value the generator will not be aware of any change. There is still no reflection, all the power applied to the input end of the line is absorbed in the terminating resistance, and the line is said to be matched.

Again because no reflections occur at the end of a correctly matched line, the ratio of the travelling waves of voltage and current, V / I, is Z_0. This enables the load presented to the feeder by the antenna to be in turn presented to the transmitter, without any change in the process. This is irrespective of the length of line employed, since the value of the characteristic impedance Z_0 is independent of the length of the line. In order to achieve maximum efficiency from a transmission line, it should be operated as close to a matched condition as possible, ie the load presented by the antenna should be arranged, either directly or by means of some impedance transformer, to present a good match to the line. However, the degree to which the load impedance can be permitted to depart from the characteristic impedance without introducing appreciable extra losses is quite large, as discussed in the section on attenuation. On the other hand, bandwidth considerations or the need to avoid load variations which could damage transmitters may impose stringent matching requirements.

The characteristic impedance is determined by the structure of the feeder and its dimensional ratios of the cross-section of the line, and not by its absolute size.

VELOCITY FACTOR

When the medium between the conductors of a transmission line is air, the travelling waves propagate along it at the same speed as waves in free space. If a dielectric material is introduced between the conductors, for insulation or support purposes, the waves will be slowed down and will no longer travel at the free-space velocity. The velocity of the waves along any line is equal to $1 / \sqrt{(LC)}$, where L and C are the distributed capacitance and inductance values. The introduction of such material increases the capacitance without increasing the inductance because the capacitance is dependent upon the dielectric constant of the material separating the two plates in the capacitor, and consequently the characteristic impedance and the velocity are both reduced by the same factor $\sqrt{\varepsilon}$. The ratio of the velocity of waves on the line to the velocity in free space is known as the velocity factor. It is as low as 0.5 for mineral or PVC insulated lines and is roughly 0.66 for solid polythene cables (ε = 2.25). Semi-air-spaced lines have a factor which varies between 0.8 and 0.95, while open-wire lines with spacers at intervals may reach 0.98.

It is important to make proper allowances for this factor in some feeder applications, particularly where the feeders are used as tuning elements or interconnecting lines in antenna arrays, or as chokes for EMC applications. For example, if the velocity factor v = 2/3, then an electrical quarter-wave line would be *physically* a sixth of a wavelength long (2/3 x 1/4 = 1/6).

In practice, the velocity factor v can be found by short circuiting a length of cable with about 3cm of wire formed into a loop and then coupling the loop to a dip oscillator. The lowest frequency at which the cable shows resonance corresponds to an electrical length of a quarter-wave; then:

$$v = \frac{f \text{ (MHz) x Length (feet)}}{246}$$

and should have a value between 0.5 and unity.

The velocity factor is only of significance in certain antenna types, for example those requiring quarter-wave 'stubs'. Open wire lines have a velocity factor of about 0.975 which means that a quarter-wavelength stub at 7MHz will be 25cm (10in) shorter than a basic electrical quarter-wavelength.

TYPES OF LINE

There are three main types of transmission line:

(a) The single wire feed arranged so that there is a true travelling wave on it.

(b) The concentric line or coaxial feeder in which there are concentric conductors, one inside the other with an insulating layer between them. The outer conductor encloses the wave.

(c) The parallel wire line with two conductors carrying equal but oppositely directed currents and voltages, ie balanced with respect to earth. Twin line, and open wire feeders fall into this category.

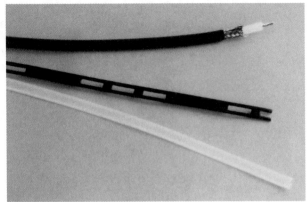

Fig 2.1 Samples of coaxial cable, black twin and ordinary translucent twin feeder .

Examples of coaxial cable and twin feeders are shown in **Fig 2.1.**

Single-wire feeders are usually connected to a point on a resonant antenna where the impedance formed by the left and right-hand portions in parallel matches the impedance of the wire. This form of feeder is now rarely used, being basically inefficient because of the losses in the return path, which is via the ground. The feeder also radiates, acting to some extent as a terminated long-wire antenna. Against this it offers the advantages of being lightweight and having a low visual impact. For short lengths (up to about half a wavelength) the losses should normally be less than 1dB.

COAXIAL LINE

The most common type of feeder used today is undoubtedly coaxial feeder or coax. As the name suggests the cable consists of two concentric conductors as shown in **Fig 2.2**. The centre conductor is almost universally made of copper. Sometimes it may be a single conductor whilst at other times it may consist of several strands.

The outer conductor is normally made from a copper braid. This enables the cable to be flexible which would not be the case if the outer conductor was solid. To improve the screening, double or even triple screened cables are sometimes used. Normally this is accomplished by placing one braid directly over another although in some instances a copper foil or tape outer may be used. By using additional layers of screening, the levels of stray pick-up and radiation are considerably reduced. More importantly for most radio amateurs this will result in lower levels of loss.

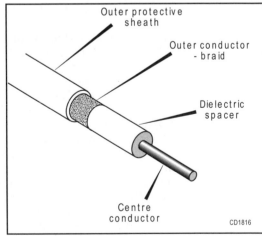

Fig 2.2 Coaxial feeder.

Between the two conductors there is an insulating dielectric. This holds the two conductors apart and in an ideal world would not introduce any loss. This dielectric may be solid or as in the case of many low-loss cables it may be semi-air-spaced because it is the dielectric that introduces most of the loss. This may be in the form of long 'tubes' in the dielectric, or a 'foam' construction where air forms a major part of the material.

Finally there is the outer cover or sheath. This serves little electrical function, but can prevent earth loops forming. It also gives a vital protection needed to prevent dirt and moisture attacking the cable. However, when burying cable it is best not to rely on the sheath. Instead use conduit or use special 'bury direct' cables that are available.

CHARACTERISTIC IMPEDANCE
The characteristic impedance of the feeder is defined by the ratio of the two conductors and the dielectric constant of the material between them. For example a diameter ratio 2.3: 1 and using an air dielectric provides a 50Ω line, whatever its overall diameter may be. If it is connected to an antenna of 50Ω radiation resistance, all the power available at the far end of the line will pass into the antenna and the impedance at the sending end of the line will also appear to be 50 Ω. (Coaxial cables can conveniently be constructed with characteristic impedance values between about 50 and 120Ω. Twin lines have higher impedances: in practice, between 80 and 600Ω. A graph of the characteristic impedance for both coaxial and two wire lines in terms of the dimensional ratios, assuming air between the conductors is shown in **Fig 2.3**.

The figures can also be calculated quite easily. The formula for concentric lines of inner and outer diameters d and D respectively is:

$$Z_0 \text{ (ohms)} = 138 \log_{10} (D / d)$$

Thus if the diameter ratio D / d is 2.3:1 the logarithm of 2.3 is 0.362 and this multiplied by the constant 138 gives Z_0 = 50Ω. If the space between conductors is filled with insulating material with a dielectric constant E (permittivity) greater than unity, the above value of Z_0 must be divided by the square root of the dielectric constant.

The usual material for insulation is polythene, which has a permittivity of 2.25. The square root of 2.25 is 1.5 so that a 'solid' polythene cable has a characteristic impedance two-thirds of the value given by the formula. Many cables have a mixed air / polythene dielectric, and for these it is necessary to estimate the effect of the dielectric.

CABLE LOSS
The loss introduced by the feeder is another important factor. Resistance loss calculated for the inner conductor accounts for about half the attenuation of new coaxial cable. The remainder is resistance loss in the outer conductor, additional resistance loss due to proximity effect arising from the close spacing between conductors, and dielectric losses in the insulating material. Radiation loss is virtually zero, provided no current flows on the outside of the cable. With most of the older types of cable there is an increase in resistance with age as a result of corrosion caused by chemicals used in the manufacture, and with cables of any age serious

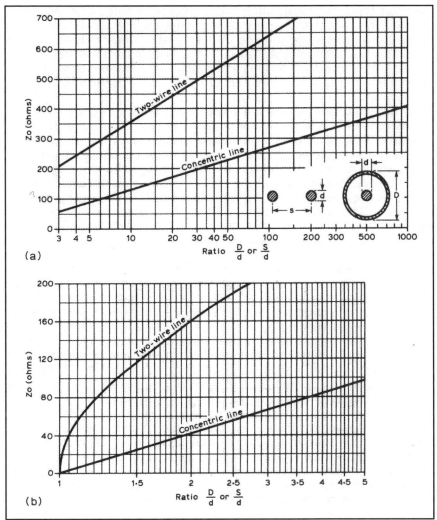

Fig 2.3 Chart giving characteristic impedances of concentric (coaxial) and two wire lines in terms of their dimensional ratios, assuming air insulation. When the space around the wires is filled with insulation, the impedance given by the chart must be divided by the square root of its dielectric constant (permittivity). This ratio is called the velocity factor because the wave velocity is reduced in the same proportion.

deterioration can result if joints are not adequately protected against moisture. A blackened inner conductor means that the cable is useless but any sign of discolouration or corrosion should be regarded with suspicion.

PROTECTING THE CABLE ENDS
The trouble with water from an engineering point of view is that it reacts chemically with practically everything. This means that it is necessary to keep it out of areas where such a reaction will cause a problem. One particular area is coaxial cable, where water getting in will tend to oxidise

the outer braid and considerably reduce its conductivity, thus increasing its loss. This means that every time coaxial cable is used outside it is necessary to give some thought to how to stop water getting in. With good quality cable being expensive, it is imperative to ensure that it remains in top condition as long as possible. John Nelson, G(W)4FRX, in an article in the January 1989 *RadCom* gives some useful ideas.

Many antennas and baluns are fitted with connector sockets and this means that the cable run to the antenna needs to be terminated in a connector. Typically these may either be a PL259 or an N-type connector. The N-type is said to be capable of keeping water out of coaxial cable if it is properly installed, although it is best not to take a chance on that being true. However, the PL259 is about as waterproof as a fishing net. Serious waterproofing is required for any connector that is to be used for antenna purposes. The best and simplest way seems to be by using self amalgamating tape. This is made by a number of companies and is available from antenna and general amateur radio stockists.

Self-amalgamating tape comes in the form of a roll of what looks like thick insulating tape but with a thin paper backing on one side. It is used in a similar way to insulating tape in so far as the backing strip is peeled off and then it is wrapped around whatever it is to be waterproofed, overlapping each winding by about 50% of its width to ensure a good seal. Keep a bit of stretch on the tape as it is wound so that it goes on under tension. It is best to start from the thinner end of the job, so to speak - meaning that if an in-line connector joining two pieces of coaxial cable is to be waterproofed, start the tape on one piece of the cable, take it over the connector and on to the other piece. If the job allows it is also good to make the joint what a professional would call 'half-lapped' - meaning that when the thickest part of the job (such as the connector) is reached, cut the tape and then start again from the other piece of cable, over-winding the second tape run on to the first so that the connector is completely covered. This will ensure that there are no 'voids' in the join in which water could condense. The aim is to get the self-amalgamating tape in intimate contact with whatever it is to be waterproofed.

What happens then is a little miracle of industrial chemistry. In a short time the separate layers of tape which have been wound on start to fuse together, so that ultimately the connector (or whatever) is completely covered with what amounts to a custom-made and fully waterproof 'boot'. Provided that the physical construction of whatever it is being waterproofed allows the self-amalgamating tape to be wound on to it, it is the best stuff to use. There is one slight snag, though. Self-amalgamating tape is actually a plastic substance called polyisobutylene, which is one of a class of thermoplastics that doesn't like the ultra-violet content of sunlight - so it tends to go brittle and crack after a year or two. No problem at all. All that needs to be done is to wrap it with a layer of ordinary PVC insulating tape. To do a really gold-plated MIL-spec job, give the final result a couple of coats of clear polyurethane varnish.

TWIN LINE FEEDER
The third type of feeder used at HF is parallel wire line. This may be in a number of forms. It is possible to buy manufactured versions of this line

having impedances between 75 and 300Ω. The most common is actually 300Ω line. This is a flat construction having the two wires covered in a plastic insulation and dielectric that is also used to space them apart, as shown in **Fig 2.4**.

A version of this feeder with a light opaque plastic is widely used for commercially-manufactured temporary VHF / FM antennas. This feeder can obviously be bought separately and can be used in a number of applications. This type does have some drawbacks as it tends to absorb moisture when used externally and this naturally alters its characteristics and the loss rises. Another type with black insulation that is slotted between the conductors is far more suitable.

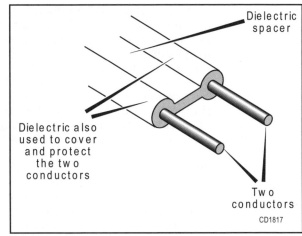

Fig 2.4 Twin feeder.

Open wire feeder, as the name suggests, is made up from wire with spacers at suitable intervals along the wire. As the spacing is greater this generally has a higher characteristic impedance.

In just the same way that the characteristic impedance of coaxial feeder was governed by the ratio of the diameters of the conductors and the dielectric between them, the equivalent is also true for twin wire feeders. However, the measurements that govern the impedance of the twin wire feeder are the diameters of the wires and the distance between them. In this way the formula used to calculate the impedance of a feeder diameter d and centre spacing S is given by the approximate formula:

Z_0 (ohms) = 276 $\log_{10}$ (2S / d)

FEEDER LOSSES
The losses in tuned lines include any loss by radiation (which is normally very small), and any resistive loss in the conductor wires. Assuming that feed lines are fabricated from 18 to 14SWG copper wires, the resistive losses are insignificant and those that exist are mostly related to the dielectric properties of the material used for the spacers.

At UHF or VHF spacers are seldom used, the wires being held taut and parallel with just air as the dielectric. Open-wire matched lines with spacers arranged at 45cm (15in) intervals will show an attenuation of 0.03dB per 30m (100ft) at 3.5MHz, rising to 0.25dB at 144MHz. This means that a 3dB power loss (half power) will only occur when the feed line is about 3 kilometres (10,000 feet) long at a frequency of 3.5MHz. Tuned lines will exhibit higher losses.

For convenience, 300Ω ribbon feeder may be used as tuned line, especially the slotted variety. The finest available ribbon feeder will have a greater loss than open-wire line, but this will still be relatively insignificant. The older type of flat 300Ω ribbon feeder, when used as a matched line, has an attenuation of 0.18dB per 30m (100ft) at 3.5MHz, rising to 1.55dB at 144MHz. However, this older ribbon detunes badly in wet weather, with the plastic dielectric absorbing moisture to give a significant increase in loss as well as a change in dielectric constant and hence the velocity factor. It has also been found that the absorbed moisture gives rise to corrosion in the wires, further worsening the performance over a period of time. The black plastic slotted variety has a better performance and its 'semi-air' spacing and water-shedding characteristics make it ideal. Its use also avoids the tedium of making up a long run of open-wire feeder.

Unscreened twin-wire feeder must not be buried or its nominal impedance may be affected, and there will then be a high SWR on the line. The twin feeder is, however, less susceptible to dampness effects than some of the 300Ω ribbon cables available, for most of the electrical field between the conductors is confined within the solid black polyethylene insulating material into which they are embedded. The black colouring helps to reduce UV damage (caused by sunlight) to the plastic, so avoid light coloured or transparent cable varieties.

REACTANCE

Tuned feeders can exhibit reactance at their feed point, and this reactance may be either inductive or capacitive depending upon the frequency, the feeder length and the length of the antenna top. With any given antenna which uses tuned feeders, the reactance will be different on each frequency band, and it can be that on one or more bands there will only be resistive impedance which is much easier to cope with when using an antenna tuning unit (ATU).

The use of an ATU, also known as an 'ASTU' (antenna system tuning unit) or 'AMU' (antenna matching unit), is essential when using an antenna with a tuned feed line. In most cases the ATU will be able to 'tune out' the reactance present, but unfortunately there is no ATU design which will cope with an infinite range of impedance or reactance, so in practice certain combinations of antenna and feeder lengths must be avoided. An antenna which appears almost impossible to match on just one amateur band may have this corrected by the addition or subtraction of feet, or tens of feet, of feed line.

OPEN-WIRE FEEDER CONSTRUCTION

Apart from the advantages of very low levels of feeder loss, open wire feeder has the advantage that it can be made for very little cost, and this can be a considerable advantage when compared with the investment that has to be made when any significant length of coaxial low loss feeder is installed.

The spacing spreaders always seem to present the greatest challenge to the ingenuity of constructors, with almost any insulator from plastic hair curlers to sections of plastic milk bottles being suitable. One solution is to use Perspex strips measuring approximately 13cm (5in) by 18mm (0.75in) wide, and cut from the scrap off cuts available at 'give away' prices at local glassworks. If the spacers are made thin, say 25 to 30mm long, the length of the leakage path from any accumulation of dust, soot and grime that can give problems in damp weather is greatly reduced.

The number of spreaders required depends on a number of factors including the thickness of the wire. Using very thin wire will mean the use of many more spreaders, and this will raise the dielectric losses of the line. A sturdy 18 SWG or, better still, 16 SWG enamelled wire is ideal. Alternatively hard-drawn, bare copper is very satisfactory. Fewer spreaders will also reduce the weight of the feed line and its pull on the antenna.

Construction needs to be undertaken with a little thought to ensure the best end result. One method is to take two equal lengths of wire. These can be tied to an outside feature such as a fence post or railing, and then pulled out tightly towards another tie point. The spacers can then all be threaded on to the wires, after which the wire ends are secured to the second tie point. The spacers must then be equally spaced along the feeder at intervals of about 45cm

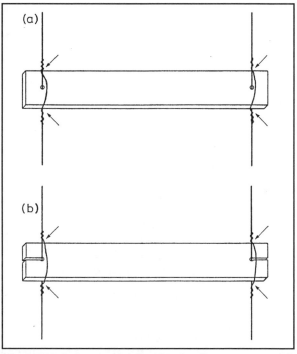

Fig 2.5 (a) An open-wire feeder line spacer with drilled holes for the wires, and wire 'retainers' to prevent slip. Spacers of this type have to be threaded on to the feeder wires before they are set into their final positions. (b) A spacer with slotted ends which can be easily fixed at any point along a completed length of feeder.

(18in). The holes in the spreaders near their ends must be just large enough to allow the wires to be pushed through. To ensure that the feeders will not slip out of position with the passage of time, some short lengths of wire can be twisted on to the feeder wires just above and below each spreader. These are indicated by the arrows in **Fig 2.5** at (a).

Instead of drilling holes in the spacers, they may be slotted as shown in Fig 2.6(b). This method allows additional spreaders to be added after the line is completed.

The very best way to make a feed line is to use a thermoplastic material for the spacers and then arrange them into their correct positions along the wires. This is followed by putting a high current through each wire in turn, in order to heat up and bond the spreaders to it. This was the way the commercial feed lines were made 30 years ago.

Avoid joins in the feeder and the antenna wire if possible, and certainly make sure that there are no kinks in the wires. The preparation and making up of feeders and doublet wires cannot be done satisfactorily indoors and a fine day is an important factor!

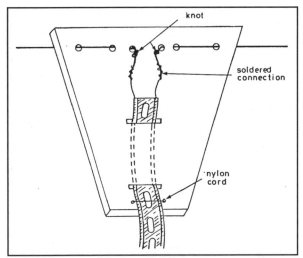

Fig 2.6 A centre block suitable for the connection of a 300Ω impedance ribbon to an antenna centre.

It is often sensible to anchor an open-wire feed line to stop excessive swaying, and this can be done with the help of nylon fishing line. This line is often stained blue, and is invisible from more than a few metres. Any bends in the feed line must be of as large a radius as possible, and there must be no sudden and sharp bends. The line must be kept as far as possible from walls, down-pipes, gutters etc, and it should also drop down from the antenna centre at a right angle for at least a quarter-wavelength at the lowest frequency to be used. If the feeder runs under one leg of the antenna top the system will become unbalanced.

A centre block suitable for the connection of a 300Ω ribbon feeder to an antenna centre is shown in **Fig 2.6**.

CONNECTORS

One essential element of using coaxial cables is that of the connectors to use, and the correct fixing of them to the cable. This may appear simple, but it is essential that the connectors are fitted correctly if they are to perform to their specification. They are not always easy to fit. A good summary about fitting connectors and the pitfalls to be avoided was provided by Roger Blackwell, G4PMK, in the May 1988 *RadCom*.

The main secret of success is using the right cable with the right connector. When buying connectors, it is important to be able to recognise good and bad types, and know what cables the good ones are for. Using the wrong connector and cable combination is sure to lead to disaster. Any information from sources such as old catalogues is likely to prove useful, especially if it is possible to get the cable cutting dimensions and equivalents lists.

Cables are commonly of one of two families: the American 'RG' (Radio Guide MIL specification) types and the British 'UR' (UniRadio) series. URM67 is equivalent to RG213, is 10.5mm diameter and is the most common feeder used with N-type and PL259 connectors. URM43 (5mm OD) is one usually used with BNC connectors, although these also fit RG58 cable since both have similar dimensions. If there is any doubt about the quality of the cable, have a look at the braid. It should cover the dielectric completely. If it doesn't, it is unlikely to be worth buying. There are a lot of so-called 'RG8' cables about these days, intended for the cheap end of the CB market, that are anything but good. Avoid them like the plague - RG8 is an obsolete designation - the modern equivalent is RG213 or URM67.

Having obtained the cable, the easy bit is over. Now to select the connector. The three most popular connector types are the UHF (PL259), BNC and N types. These will be covered in some detail, and a few others will be mentioned later. It goes without saying, of course, that one of the universe's natural laws is that the number of connector types in any shack tends towards a maximum. However, when new ones need to be bought, buy from a reputable source but there are also some good surplus bargains at rallies, hamfests and the like.

It cannot be too widely known that the 'UHF' connector is no good much beyond 200MHz, because the impedance through the plug-socket junction is not 50Ω. The suitability of N and BNC connectors for use at UHF and beyond is due to their maintaining the system impedance (normally 50Ω) through the connector. PL259 plugs, like the RG8 cable they were intended for, have a lot of nasty imitations. Beware of any that do not have PTFE insulation. They may be suitable, but many cheap types are lossy and badly made. They may be adequate for receiving, but not for transmitting 400W PEP at 144MHz. The plating should be good quality (silver solders best, although some proprietary plated finishes are just about as good), and there should be two or more solder holes in the body for soldering to the braid. There should be two small tags on the outer mating edge of the plug, which locate in the serrated ring of the socket and stop the body rotating. If small diameter cable is to be used, obtain the correct reducer. Often two types are available: for 75Ω and 50Ω cable. The 50Ω type is often called UG175. Using the wrong one is certain to cause a disaster. It is necessary to buy the plugs and reducers at the same time because some manufacturers use different reducer threads.

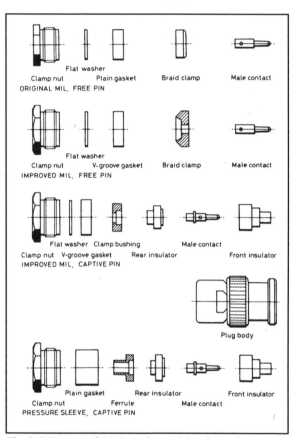

Fig 2.7 Types of BNC and N cable clamps.

With BNC, TNC (like the BNC but threaded) N and C (like N but bayonet) types, life can be more complicated. All these connectors are available in 50 and 75Ω versions. Be sure you get the right one. All of these connectors have evolved over the years and consequently there are a number of different types. The variations are mostly associated with the cable clamping and centre pin securing method. The original cable clamp type is usually called 'unimproved MIL', the later modification the 'improved', but the best for most uses is the 'pressure-sleeve' type. If buying new, and for normal use, opt for the pressure-sleeve type because it is much easier to fit. However, if it is to be used with some of the double-braided PTFE-dielectric cable such as

RG142, it is easier to use the older clamp types, although the pressure-sleeve type will fit properly with care.

All original clamp types use a free centre pin that is held in place by its solder joint on to the inner conductor. Captive contact types have a two-part centre insulator between which fits the shoulder on the centre pin. Improved MIL clamp types may have either free or captive contacts. Pressure-sleeve types have a captive centre pin. As an aid to identification, **Fig 2.7** shows these types. Pressure clamp captive pin types are easy to spot; they have a ferrule or 'top hat' that assists in terminating the braid, a two-piece insulator and a centre pin with a shoulder. Unimproved clamp types have a washer, a plain gasket, a cone-ended braid clamp and a single insulator, often fixing inside the body. Improved types have a washer, a thin ring gasket with a V-groove and usually a conical braid clamp with more of a shoulder.

Chapter 3
The Dipole Antenna

The wire dipole is a very effective antenna that can be constructed and installed very easily and for only a small cost. Yet, despite this, the half-wave version of the dipole has become the standard against which other radiating systems are judged and it remains as perhaps the most effective yet simple single-band antenna, and one which can virtually be guaranteed to perform well even when used in far-from-ideal situations.

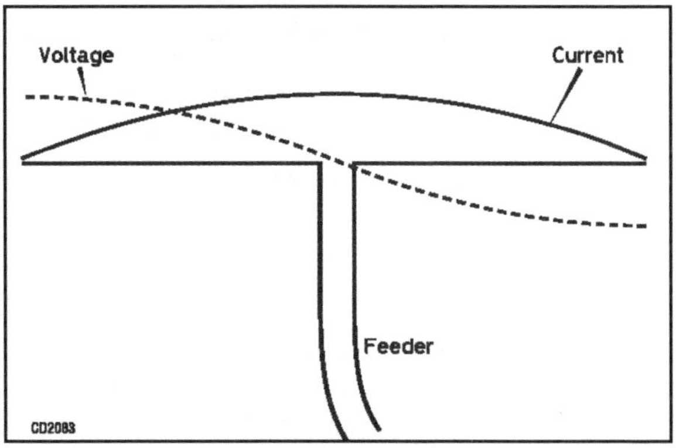

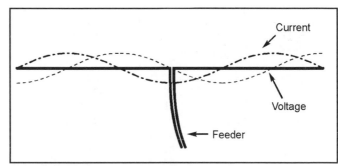

Fig 3.1 A basic dipole antenna with the voltage and current waveforms.

As the name suggested it contains two legs or poles - hence the name. The most common form is the half-wave dipole, which (not surprisingly) is an electrical half-wavelength long. The basic format for a half-wave dipole along with the voltage and current waveforms can be seen in **Fig 3.1**. The voltage rises to a maximum at either end and falls to a minimum at the centre, whereas the current is at its minimum at the end and its maximum in the centre. Its feed point in the centre forms a low impedance point suitable for many of the feeders available, but more of this later.

A dipole does not have to be a half-wavelength long. A three half-wavelength version can be seen in **Fig 3.2**. Again the points of voltage maximum are at either end and at a minimum in the centre. Likewise the current is at its minimum at either end and maximum in the centre.

Fig 3.2 A three half-wavelength dipole.

DIPOLE LENGTHS
A resonant half-wavelength of wire will be somewhat shorter than its name implies. RF energy in free space (electromagnetic radiation) can travel at the speed of light, but when moving along a conductor it travels more slowly. At HF (between 1.8 and 30MHz) wires exhibit 'skin effect' - most of the RF energy flows along the outer surface of the conductor. A practical half-wave antenna made from wire needs end supports; each end usually being terminated with an antenna insulator. The capacitance

between the ends of dipole and its supports, even when the supporting material is non-metallic, gives rise to 'end effect'. This effect additionally loads the wire capacitively and contributes towards its shortening from the theoretical half-wavelength.

The theoretical half-wavelength may be calculated from the expression:

Theoretical half wavelength (metres) = 150 / f(MHz)

or

Theoretical half-wavelength (feet) = 492 / f(MHz)

To take account of the end effect and the use of insulators, the length may be calculated by using either:

Antenna length (metres) = 143 / f(MHz)

or

Antenna length (feet) = 468 / f(MHz) feet.

When using nylon rope it has been suggested that no insulators are required. In his book *HF Antennas for All Locations* (published by the RSGB), Les Moxon, G6XN, suggests that when no insulators are used a half-wavelength can be found by using either 478 / f(MHz) feet or 145.7 / f(MHz) metres.

A further factor which influences antenna resonant length is the diameter of the wire used for that antenna. The formulae that have been quoted are for typical wire dimensions and typical antenna lengths are shown below in **Table 3.1**. This provides length details for the amateur HF bands both when using insulators or nylon rope.

Frequency		Length		
	With insulators		**Without insulators**	
(kHz)	**(feet)**	**(metres)**	**(feet)**	**(metres)**
1850	252' 11"	77.29	258' 5"	78.75
1950	240' 0"	73.33	245' 1"	74.71
3550	131' 10"	40.28	134' 8"	41.04
3750	124' 9"	38.13	127' 5"	38.85
7050	66' 4"	20.28	67' 10"	20.66
10,100	46' 4"	14.15	47' 4"	14.42
14,100	33' 2"	10.14	33' 11"	10.33
14,250	32' 10"	10.03	33' 6"	10.22
18,100	25' 10"	7.90	26' 5"	8.04
21,100	22' 2"	6.77	22' 8"	6.90
21,300	21' 11"	6.71	22' 5"	6.84
24,940	18' 9"	5.73	19' 2"	5.84
28,100	16' 8"	5.08	17' 0"	5.18
28,500	16' 5"	5.01	16' 9"	5.11
29,000	16' 1"	4.93	16' 6"	5.02
29,500	15' 10"	4.84	16' 2"	4.93

Table 3.1. Lengths of half-wave dipoles.

DIPOLE IMPEDANCES

A half-wave transmitting antenna, when energised and resonant, will have high RF voltages at its ends with theoretically zero RF currents there. This means that the ends of a half-wave dipole in free space will have an infinitely high impedance, but in practice in the real world there will always be some leakage from its ends and into the supporting insulators. This means that in reality the impedance at the dipole ends is close to 100,000Ω, a value which depends upon the wire or element thickness. At a distance of approximately one-sixteenth wavelength from either end it is 1000Ω, and at the dipole centre, where the current is greatest and the RF voltage is low, the impedance is also low.

If it were made from an infinitely thin conductor wire, our theoretical dipole in free space would have at its centre an impedance of about 73Ω. Such an antenna is impossible in the material world, and a practical half-wave dipole made from wire will have an impedance at its centre at resonance close to 65Ω. Antennas fabricated from tubing have lower values at their centres, of between 55 and 60Ω. These impedance values also depend upon the height of the antenna above ground, as will be shown later.

The very high values of self-impedance at the ends of a half-wave wire makes end-feeding difficult, and this is why breaking the wire at its centre and connecting the inner ends so formed to a low-impedance feed line makes a convenient and efficient coupling and match. Suitable feeder is available in the form of twin-lead or coaxial cable, which both have design impedances lying between 50 and 75Ω. These present a good match to dipole centres.

At exact resonance the impedance at the centre of a half-wave dipole is like a pure resistance. At any other frequencies the same dipole will have either inductive or capacitive reactance at its feed point. If the dipole is too short to be resonant the reactance is capacitive and when it is too long the reactance becomes inductive. In either case there will be problems in matching the 70Ω feeder to the dipole and if the reactances are great, there will be a high SWR on the feeder and considerable power loss.

ANTENNA Q

At resonance there will appear to be pure resistance at the dipole centre feed point but, if the antenna is too long or too short for the frequency in use, some reactance will also be present there. Half-wave dipoles which are too long exhibit inductive reactance at their feed point, and those too short will show a capacitive reactance. This reactance will make it more difficult to feed the wire or effect a full transfer of power from the feeder. The mismatch will also result in SWR readings above unity, and these will become progressively worse as the antenna becomes more off-tune.

A half-wave antenna is something like a conventional tuned circuit where the Q, or 'Quality factor', is largely determined by the resistance of the coil. Losses in the capacitor used in the circuit are generally small and are not so significant in the determination of Q. A high-Q tuned circuit exhibits very sharp tuning (selectivity) and this is also the case when an antenna has a high Q.

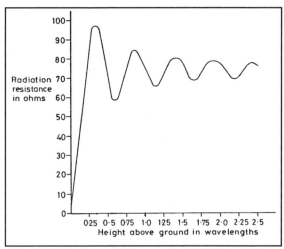

Fig 3.3 Radiation resistance of a half-wave dipole as a function of height above the ground (*The ARRL Antenna Book*).

Using thin wires lowers the bandwidth of a half-wave antenna, but not dramatically. However, short wires that are brought into resonance will exhibit high Q. The shorter the wire in terms of wavelength, the higher the Q. Small changes in the transmitting frequency away from the antenna resonances will give rise to a rapid rise in the reactance at the feed point.

Thicker wire will lower the Q, reduce resistive loss and make the half-wave dipole less frequency conscious. It is therefore best to ensure that such an antenna is made from the thickest possible wire consistent with such factors as the pull on the antenna supports, windage and sag.

DIPOLE HEIGHT

The height of a horizontal dipole above the ground as a ratio of its design frequency is important (see the standard curves of feed impedance against height in **Fig 3.3**). When below about half a wavelength high the radiation resistance at the feed point will be reduced, and down at a height of just one-tenth of a wavelength it will only be 25Ω. This means that a dipole fed from a standard type of low impedance feeder will suffer a considerable mismatch when near the ground. One-tenth of a wavelength is about 15m (50ft) on 1.8MHz and as little as a metre (3ft) on 28MHz. This helps to explain why low dipoles on the lower frequency bands are far from efficient radiators.

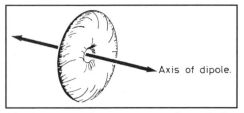

Fig 3.4 A crude representation of the radiation from a half-wave dipole antenna in free space. Practical antenna systems are, however, influenced by ground reflection and their radiation patterns are much modified.

A horizontal half-wave antenna, if at least a half-wavelength above ground, will radiate most of its applied power at right angles to the line or axis of the wire. Its radiation pattern may be visualised as having the shape of a torus or doughnut, with the wire running through the centre hole (**Fig 3.4**). About 40° on either side of the broadside maxima of radiation the power falls to half, ie -3dB, and it will fall rapidly as the angle increases.

Theoretically there should be little or no radiation off the wire ends, but in practice there will remain some radiation at high angles to the horizon from both ends, which might prove useful for short-range work. The horizontal radiation pattern at both 30° and the low angle of 9° may be seen in **Fig 3.5**. The 30° high-angle radiation from a half-wave dipole at a height of half a wavelength will tend to be from one to two S-points greater than the low-angle radiation needed for DX working in most directions (ie, about 5 to 10dB better), and emphasises the fact that a half-wave dipole is a general-purpose, 'all-round' antenna type, good for both semi-local and distant working.

From the ends, however, there is little low-angle radiation, and here it is as much as three to four S-points down from the maxima at right angles to the wire. This explains why a dipole is best arranged to be at right angles to the areas to be worked, especially for long-distance communication.

When lower than a half-wavelength from the ground, a greater proportion of the transmitted power will leave the antenna at high angles. This makes it ideal for short haul communications. Although in theory a dipole at a height less than half a wavelength would not be ideal, in practice it is still possible to use it for long haul communications. For example, a dipole for 160m at a height of 30m would make a highly effective antenna as it will be well clear of any obstructions. Even though much of the power will be radiated upwards, the power that is radiated at a low angle will be subject to less absorption by local objects than that radiated by many other antennas such as a vertical at a lower height. Thus even though antennas for the low frequency bands are unlikely to be raised to heights that are theoretically required, nevertheless they are able to provide excellent service.

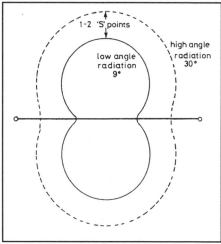

Fig 3.5 The horizontal polar diagram of a half-wave dipole at a height of half a wavelength above the ground, showing the considerable high-angle radiation (at 30°) off the ends of the wire. The low-angle radiation is mainly at right angles to the wire and is from 5 to 10dB down relative to the 30° radiation.

The vertical radiation patterns of horizontal antennas at different heights above the ground ranging from an eighth-wavelength to two wavelengths can be seen in **Fig 3.6**. In all these examples it is assumed that the antennas are above a perfectly conducting ground.

A PRACTICAL DIPOLE ANTENNA
There is no doubt that the simplest and yet most effective all-purpose, single-band antenna for the amateur, which can be guaranteed to work well without trimming or tuning adjustments so long as it conforms to the basic design parameters, is the half-wave dipole.

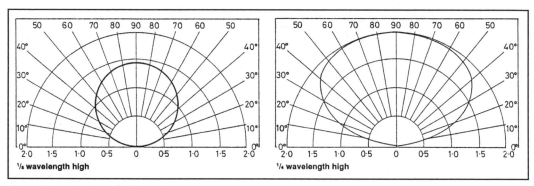

Fig 3.6 Vertical radiation patterns of horizontal antenna at differing heights above a perfectly conducting ground (*The ARRL Antenna Book*).

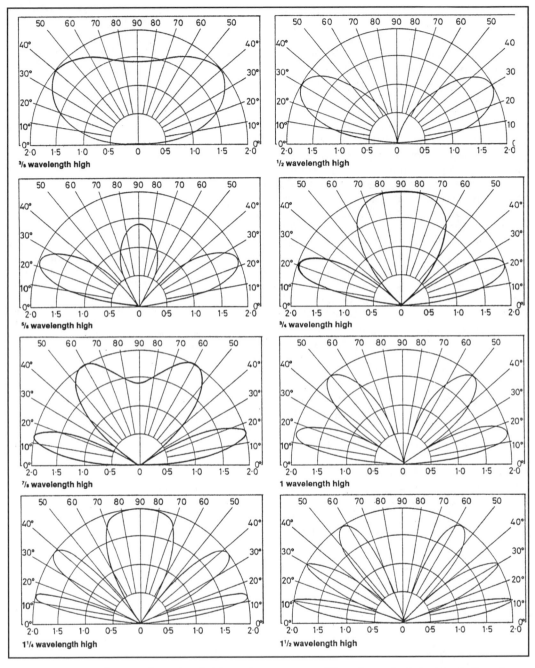

The top length of this antenna may either be calculated or taken from Table 3.1, and almost any kind of copper wire can be used. For permanent or semi-permanent installations 16 or 18SWG hard-drawn copper is to be preferred, and for experimental and temporary antennas most types of stranded and plastic-covered wire can be used. The resonant frequency of an antenna made from this wire is said to fall by 3 to 5% but the author has never noticed such an effect. This lowering of frequency may,

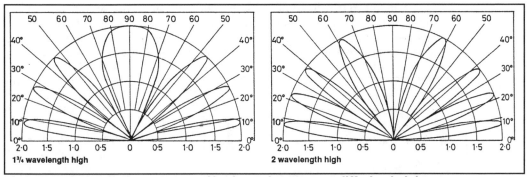

Fig 3.6 Vertical radiation patterns of horizontal antenna at differing heights above a perfectly conducting ground (*The ARRL Antenna Book*).

however, become noticeable when making and testing wire beams, especially those with quad loops as driven and parasitic elements.

If any antenna end insulators are to be used, those made from Pyrex glass are perhaps the best, and when the antenna ends are close to a metal mast more than one insulator at each end is to be preferred. Nylon or Terylene cords may be tied directly to the antenna wire ends (knotted), and they will make effective insulators if more than about 2m in length.

The antenna maker must bear in mind the change in resonant lengths which are induced by this technique (see Table 3.1), and cut his dipole longer than it would be if normal end insulators were to be used. Without end insulators the suggested 2m or more of cord between the antenna and the fixing point will present a very low leakage path even in wet weather. Although ultra-violet energy (present in sunlight) can bring on a deterioration in the structure of non-organic ropes, the author has had nylon cords in use for many years with no apparent ill effects.

If antenna insulators are used the length of the resonant top of the antenna must also include the furthest ends of the loops which pass through the insulators (**Fig 3.7**). The inch or so involved here can be important on the higher frequency bands, but of course is nothing to worry about on 1.8 or 3.5MHz. If joins are required in the top wire it is best to solder and weatherproof them. Try to avoid joins towards the centre of the dipole, because here the levels of current increase and any resistance introduced in a join will increase the resistive losses and reduce the radiated power. Further away from the centre, as the impedance rises, the effect of any introduced resistance is much less critical.

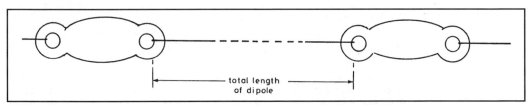

total length
of dipole

Fig 3.7 The end insulators of a dipole antenna, showing that the total length of the antenna includes the wrap-round at the tie points. Although small, such additions could detune the antenna on 21MHz and higher.

The dipole top is broken at the half-way point and here an insulator must be inserted. This point is at low RF potential and low impedance so the insulation need not be high. Using expensive glazed ceramic or glass centre insulators is a waste of money and most plastics such as Perspex, acetate or similar insulating material may be used. The centre blocks are best fabricated in the shape of a 'T' (**Fig 3.8**) or a 'Y' so that there is some way to anchor securely the top few inches of feeder. When using either twin-wire 75Ω feeder or heavier coaxial cable there must not be any strain put on to the connections to the dipole wires. All antennas will sway or swing even during relatively calm weather conditions; this can easily induce metal fatigue and an early demise of feeders high up where they cannot be observed. Fig 3.8 shows suggested anchoring methods for both types of feeder.

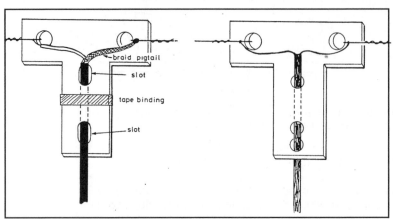

Fig 3.8 Centre 'T' blocks of an insulating material which may be used at the centre of a dipole antenna. Coaxial cable feeder, being heavier, will require more support than the twin-wire 75Ω type of feeder. Almost any insulating material which is weatherproofed may be employed for the centre blocks. No strain must be put on the soldered connections to the dipole halves.

The dipole feeder should run down vertically for at least a quarter-wavelength before it bends to run to the house or shack, and if possible it should avoid running below and in line with the antenna top. A feeder beneath the leg of a dipole antenna will unbalance the system and will lower feed point impedance. A useful and tidy way to arrange a coaxial feeder is to run it vertically down from the antenna to the ground and then bury it a few inches down on its run to the shack. Obviously if twin or open wire feeder is used this cannot be buried.

When coaxial cable is used to feed the dipole some extra care is needed where it connects to the antenna. The outer jacket of the cable should be stripped for about 10cm (4in) and then just above the new termination of the outer sleeve a hole is made through the copper braid. The insulated 'inner' may then be pulled out through this hole. In this way the braid 'pigtail' will be strong and unlikely to fray away or weaken, especially if its end is tinned with solder. The feeders must be soldered to the antenna wires and then the joints effectively weatherproofed.

There are some amateurs who deprecate coaxial feed to dipoles and advise the use of 1:1 baluns at the feed point. Although the use of coaxial feeder with a dipole does not result in a true balanced system, it actually does work well in practice without resort to baluns. It is, however, especially important that any coaxial feeder comes down vertically from the feed point, and then preferably lies along or under the ground on the remainder of its run.

Although unbalanced feeders have a number of advantages when used with any antenna, there are also some disadvantages that need to be noted:

♦ There may be RF currents induced on to the outer braid of the cable if no balun is used.
♦ The outer shield may radiate if no balun is used and this may cause interference to televisions or other equipment under some circumstances.
♦ Similarly the coaxial feeder may pick up interference. As the feeder is likely to pass near to the house, there could be additional levels of electrical interference picked up.
♦ There is a greater sensitivity to nearby objects such as masts, telephone and other overhead wires, buildings or trees.
♦ Losses can be high if the cable weathers badly and inside corrosion begins.
♦ Coaxial cable is heavy and can pull the top wire down considerably, so inducing tension strains.

Where there is no restriction in the location of the antenna and the use of only one dipole is contemplated, it is best to run it from north to south. In this way most of the world will be covered - there are comparatively few populated areas directly north and south of the UK. Similar analyses can be carried out for other countries where antennas may need to be erected. An examination of a great circle map for the required country will give a quick summary of the optimum direction for the antenna.

An extra small dividend is available when a dipole is cut for the 7MHz band, for then it will also work fairly well as a centre-fed 1.5-wavelength wire on the 21MHz band. It will, however, have quite a different radiation pattern to a standard dipole, but show a little gain over a dipole cut for 21MHz in its preferred directions of radiation.

MATCHING
Mention was made earlier of the use of an ATU (antenna tuning, or matching, unit) when twin-wire feeder is used. The use of an ATU brings many advantages and when properly adjusted will ensure that a good match is obtained and a low value of VSWR seen by the transceiver - an essential requirement for most modern units. In addition to this, an ATU provides an additional tuned circuit on the transmitting or receiving frequency which aids selectivity, reduces cross-modulation effects from strong off-frequency signals and, most importantly, cuts down any radiation of harmonics or spurious signals.

Some solid-state transceivers may suffer damage if operated using load impedances that do not meet the nominal 50Ω requirement. Some designs automatically reduce power output when used with a VSWR of around 3:1 or more. The use of an ATU can help to prevent such problems arising, especially when a dipole is being used away from its design frequency and when therefore it does not match its feeder. Such a mismatch to the antenna cannot be avoided and there will be of course some small loss of power radiated, but the use of an ATU in such a situation will ensure that the transceiver will be 'fooled' into behaving as if all is unchanged despite the mismatch. An ATU should of course also be used in conjunction with an SWR meter, and if this instrument is connected between the end of the feeder and the ATU, any mismatch which occurs when the dipole is used on either side of its design frequency will be very noticeable. At best, even on the dipole's resonant frequency, it is unlikely that the SWR reading will be perfect unity, for it is very difficult to achieve a perfect match to either 50 or 72Ω at the dipole centre. This is because the nominal antenna impedance is dependent upon such factors as height, the type of ground beneath the antenna, nearby objects and so on.

Although it is necessary to keep the SWR as low as reasonably possible to enable modern transmitters or transceivers to operate satisfactorily, as far as the antenna itself is concerned, it can operate with a much higher SWR without its performance being unduly degraded. It needs an SWR reading of 3.7:1 to double feed line losses and it is unlikely that even the most ill-fashioned or awkwardly positioned dipole would present such a high mismatch. If the SWR reading lies between unity and 1.5:1 any mismatch loss will be negligible. At such an SWR reading the total line losses will then only be the cable losses multiplied by a factor of 1.1.

Before leaving the topic of SWR on feed lines it must also be stressed that a feeder connecting to a half-wave dipole antenna can be of any length, so long as its nominal impedance equals the impedance at the dipole centre. If any addition or subtraction of feed line greatly affects the SWR present, it means that there must be a serious mismatch at the antenna connection.

INCREASING THE BANDWIDTH OF A DIPOLE
It has already been stated that a low-Q half-wave wire will have a wider

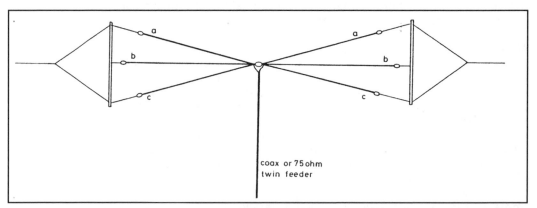

Fig 3.9 How a broadbanded 'bow-tie' or 'fantail' dipole can be constructed. The three dipoles a, b and c are cut to resonate at the band edges and centre band frequency. This technique will allow a single antenna to be used on the 3.5MHz band. A half-wave dipole cut to resonate at the LF end of this band will be 2.13m (7ft) too long at the HF end. On the higher-frequency bands the width of the band relative to the frequency is small, and a single dipole cut to mid-band will suffice.

bandwidth than a high-Q one which has been made with very thin conductor wire. One way to ensure that a dipole covers an entire band (especially on the 3.5MHz and 1.8MHz bands) is to use a very thick wire for the antenna. Two or three thinner wires can be put in parallel to achieve this, but a better way is to use a 'fantail' or 'bow tie' arrangement (see **Fig 3.9**), which will provide a low SWR right across the band.

On the higher frequencies any normal antenna wire will of course be thicker in terms of wavelength, and therefore the antenna Q will be lower. Despite this, those who intend CW operation at the LF end of the 28MHz band, together with some working on FM or satellite reception above 29MHz, might find they need to increase the bandwidth of the antenna. A half-wave wire cut for 29MHz is around a third of a metre shorter than one for 28MHz; a difference of about 6%.

When using a 'fantail' arrangement, there may be three wires used in total and the outer ones are made a little shorter than the centre one to resonate at the HF end of the band, whereas the centre wire should be cut to resonate at the LF end. The wire arrangement can be altered of course, so that the shorter wire lies in the centre between the two LF wires, or instead all three wires can be of different lengths, so covering HF, LF and mid-band frequencies. A separation of about a metre between the wires is adequate, and they may either go to different end tie points or more conveniently attach to plastic or wooden spreaders (via insulators). Table 3.1 can be used for determining the wire lengths of broadband multi-dipoles.

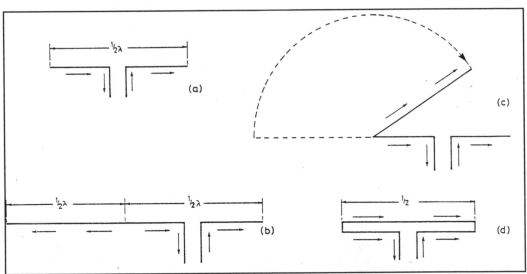

Fig 3.10 (a) The instantaneous current flow in a half-wave centre-fed antenna. The currents along both halves of the wire top are in phase. (b) The current in the added half-wavelength is in opposition to that in the dipole. (c) If this added half wavelength is now brought across as shown, its RF current will no longer be 180 degrees out of phase with the current in the dipole. (d) By joining the end of the added section to the right-hand end of the dipole the current in both wires of the new folded dipole will be in phase; each wire having half of the total current.

FOLDED DIPOLES

Another form of dipole is the folded dipole. It is often used as a part of more complicated antennas such as Yagis, but it is also a useful antenna on its own. It has the advantages that it has a higher impedance and a wider bandwidth than an ordinary dipole. As such it is very useful in many applications. **Fig 3.10** gives an understanding of how the antenna operates, showing where the currents flow within the antenna.

Fig 3.10(a) shows a conventional half-wave dipole, the arrows indicating the instantaneous currents along its two wires. They are in phase and there is no cancellation of energy. When another conductor is connected, as shown in Fig 3.10(b), the current in this new conductor will not flow in the same direction as that in the original dipole. This is because of the rule for reversal of direction of current in alternate half-wave sections along a wire. The fact that the extension to the ends of the dipole is 'folded' back makes the currents in the new section flow in the same direction as those in the original dipole. The currents along both the half-waves are therefore in phase and the antenna will radiate with the same radiation patterns etc as a simple half-wave dipole.

The feed impedance is an important feature of a folded dipole. The power supplied to a folded dipole is evenly shared between the two conductors which make up the antenna, so therefore the RF current I in each conductor is reduced to I/2. This is a half of the current value (assuming that the same power is applied) at the centre of the common half-wave dipole, so the impedance is raised. The power in watts is equal to P x R so, by halving the current at the feed point yet still maintaining the same power level, the impedance at that point will be four times greater.

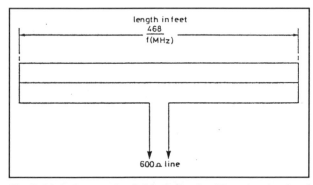

Dipole: 280W Power = PR
(I = 2A, R = 70 ohms)
Therefore:
4 x 70 = 280W

Folded dipole: 280W
I^2R (when I = 1A)
I x R = 280W
so R = 280 ohms

This means that a two-conductor folded dipole will have a feed impedance of 280Ω, which is close to the impedance of 300Ω twin feeder. It can therefore be satisfactorily matched and fed with this feeder, and have a low SWR along the feed line.

Fig 3.11 A three-wire folded dipole. If each wire is of equal diameter the total current will then be shared equally between the three wires. The impedance at the feed point will then be nine times that of a conventional half-wave dipole (9 x 70Ω = 630Ω) and will be a close match to a 600Ω impedance feed line.

If a third conductor is added to the folded dipole (**Fig 3.11**), the antenna current will be evenly split three ways and the impedance at the feed point will be nine times greater than the nominal 70Ω impedance of a simple dipole. Such a three-wire dipole with its feed impedance of 630Ω will make a good match to a 600Ω feeder. This feeder may be made from 18SWG wires which are spaced at 75mm (3in).

A four-wire folded dipole will have a feed impedance of 1120Ω, which is 16 times the impedance of a simple dipole antenna. The feed impedances of the folded dipoles so far considered will only apply when their conductor wires are of equal diameter, and are in the same plane. A wide range of step-up ratios may be achieved when tubing elements of differing diameters and spacings are used, but the calculations involved in respect of such arrangements are outside the scope of this book.

The fact that the feed impedance of a folded dipole is increased is used in the design of Yagi and other beam antennas that use parasitic elements, ie elements that pick up and re-radiate the power and are not directly driven by a feed line. The fact that the elements are placed close together in these designs means that the feed impedance of the driven element falls, often to very low values. A figure between 10 and 15Ω is not unusual. By using a folded dipole the feed impedance can be multiplied by four to bring it back up to a value which presents a good match to 50Ω coax.

Resonant length
A folded dipole which is made with two wires spaced several inches apart will have a resonant length which is equal to that of a simple half-wave dipole (**Fig 3.12(a)**, ie 468 / f(MHz) feet. However, if the antenna top is fashioned from 300Ω ribbon or a similar solid dielectric line, the velocity factor of such a line must be taken into account. The older unslotted

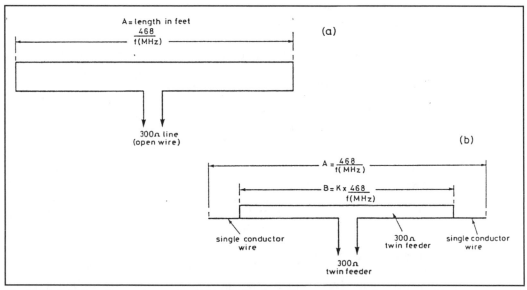

Fig 3.12 (a) The dimensions of a folded-dipole antenna using wires spaced between 6 and 12in. apart. (b) When 300W ribbon is used to make a folded dipole the velocity factor of this material must be taken into consideration when calculating its length. Small end wires are used to make up the full half-wavelength of the folded-dipole top. *K* is the velocity factor of the ribbon cable and can range from 0.8 (the old type of ribbon) to 0.87 (the newer slotted variety).

300Ω ribbon has a velocity factor K of 0.8 whereas the new slotted variety has a K of 0.87. The resonant half-wave length of 468 / f(MHz) feet must be multiplied by the value of K to determine the length of a folded dipole when it is made with 300Ω ribbon.

This will be shorter than the normal dipole length and it is brought up to resonance by the addition of short wire extensions at the dipole ends (see **Fig 3.12(b)**. **Table 3.2** gives the calculated lengths of both types of ribbon feeder when they are used as the main sections of folded dipoles on eight of the amateur HF bands.

Band(MHz)	'B' Top section using 300Ω slotted ribbon. K = 0.87 Metres / Feet		'B' Top section using 300Ω flat ribbon K= 0.8 Metres / Feet		'A' Full length of dipole = 469 / f(MHz) feet Metres / Feet	
3.5	34.44m	113' 1"	31.69m	104' 0"	39.62m	130' 0"
7	17.72m	58' 2"	16.3m	53' 5"	20.37m	66' 10"
10.1	12.28m	40' 4"	11.29m	37' 1"	14.12m	46' 4"
14.15	8.76m	28' 9"	8.06m	26' 5"	10.07m	33' 1"
18.1	6.85m	22' 6"	6.30m	20' 8"	7.87m	25' 10"
21.2	5.85m	19' 2"	5.37m	17' 8"	6.72m	22' 1"
24.94	4.97m	16' 4"	4.57m	15' 0"	5.71m	18' 9"
29	4.27m	14' 0"	3.93m	12' 11"	4.91m	16' 1"

Table 3.2 Lengths for folded dipoles using 300Ω ribbon cable.

A useful 'spin-off' from the use of a folded dipole is its inherent lower Q and its flatter impedance / frequency characteristic which produces a better bandwidth than that of a simple dipole.

A folded dipole cannot be used at twice its fundamental frequency or at any even multiple of that frequency, as the currents in the two conductors will be out of phase and will cancel. If used on these frequencies it will behave like a continuation of the feed line and the RF currents will be out of phase. On its third and other odd multiples of its resonant frequency, however, a folded dipole will have the proper current distribution and phasing to give effective radiation, and additionally its feed impedance will be close to 300Ω, although the radiation pattern will become that of a centre-fed wire three or more half wavelengths long.

Feeding a folded dipole
The simplest way to feed a folded dipole is with a 300Ω impedance balanced-line. This can be either of the solid dielectric 'ribbon' type or instead made up in the open wire 'ladder' manner as described in Chapter 2. At the bottom end of this feed line a suitable ATU must be used to provide a match into 50Ω.

It is often inconvenient to arrange for a long run of balanced feeder, and in this case the feed method which is illustrated in **Fig 3.13(a)** may be adopted. Here the 300Ω line drops vertically from the centre of the antenna to almost ground level, where it connects to a balun B, which must have a step-down ratio of 4:1, providing an unbalanced output impedance of 75Ω. A length of 75Ω coaxial cable can then be led from the balun to the operating position, being buried if necessary. A matching unit in the form of an ATU must still be used in order to match the 75Ω impedance of the cable to the nominal 50Ω of most transmitter output sections.

Suitable baluns can be purchased and this is a course to be recommended when high-power operation is contemplated, but efficient baluns can be easily made for power levels of 100 watts or less, as shown in **Fig 3.13(b)**. Simple 4:1 and other baluns can be readily constructed from short lengths of enamelled copper wire and ferrite rods of the type which are used in MW / LW broadcast receivers.

Folded dipole construction

The best and most mechanically sound way to construct a half-wave folded wire dipole is shown in **Fig 3.14**. A single length of wire (preferably single-strand copper) makes up the two parts of the dipole, and they can be held apart by the use of a few spreaders which are made from a weatherproof insulating material. The RF voltages towards the ends of folded dipoles are not very high so there is little likelihood of large losses from the use of such spreaders.

The fact that the top and the bottom dipole sections are not exactly parallel will have almost no effect upon the performance or the feed impedance of such an antenna. Instead of using end insulators such as those shown

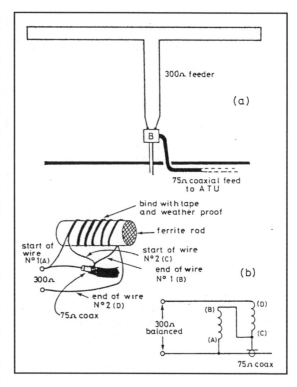

Fig 3.13 (a) The 300Ω impedance of the feeder to a folded dipole can be reduced to a value of 75Ω (unbalanced) by using a 4:1 step-down balun. (b) Constructional details of a suitable 4:1 balun which uses a short piece of ferrite rod as its core. This design was developed by Les Moxon, G6XN.

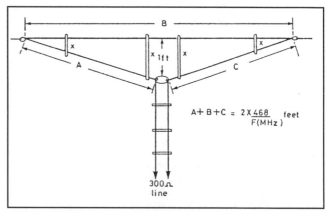

Fig 3.14 An 'all-wire' folded dipole. The feeder can be the open-wire type or a length of 300Ω ribbon. A disadvantage of ribbon feeder is that its characteristics can change when it is wet.

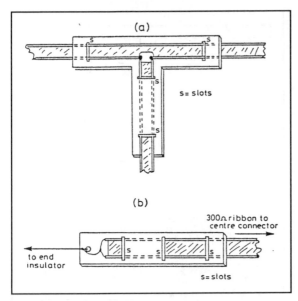

Fig 3.15 (a) How a 'T' shaped piece of insulating material (Perspex or similar) can be used to make the centre section of a folded dipole made with

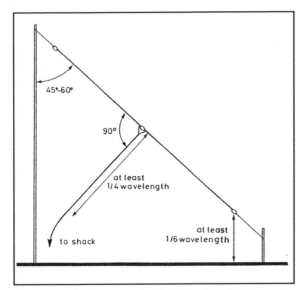

Fig 3.16 A half-wave sloping dipole which can be put up in a small space and which will be useful for long-distance working. Most of its low-angle radiation is towards the low end of the antenna but there is also considerable radiation at high angles in other directions. If possible non-metallic masts should be used to support a 'sloper', but when this cannot be arranged ensure that the mast length is not close to a half-wavelength at the operating frequency.

in the diagram, lengths of nylon or similar cord can be used as both insulators and supports. A horizontal folded dipole, like a simple half-wave dipole, may be arranged to slope or be vertical, and will then show the same changes in its radiation patterns and polarisation as the dipole. A folded dipole has no power gain advantage over a basic half-wave dipole.

When 300Ω ribbon is used as the whole or just a part of the radiating element (and as the feeder) of a folded dipole, some care is needed to reduce any physical stress upon the ribbon and the connections. In **Fig 3.15** (a) illustrates how a suitable centre connecting block can be made. A material such as the ubiquitous Perspex can be cut or drilled (beware as drilling Perspex is not easy; great care should be taken) and it also has adequate insulation characteristic for most weather conditions. Dabs of silicone rubber or other similar water-repelling substance should be applied to the soldered connections at the dipole centre for protection.

A folded dipole made from both ribbon and wire sections as already described (see Table 3.2) presents mechanical problems where they join, but the use of Perspex strips as shown in Fig 3.15 (b) is suggested to overcome these difficulties. This approach does not place undue strain upon the junction of the end wires with the ribbon, and the friction on the ribbon where it is threaded through the three narrow slots will prevent slippage.

SLOPING DIPOLES
Horizontal half-wave dipoles require two end supports and it is not always possible to provide these in some awkward locations. In such situations a single support, preferably a non-metallic mast or a high point on a building, will suffice, and then the antenna can be arranged to slope down towards the ground at an angle lying somewhere between 45 and 60°

(**Fig 3.16**). The sloping half-wave dipole should have its lower end at least one-sixth of a wavelength above ground, and its feeder should come away from the radiator at 90° for at least a quarter of a wavelength. If coaxial feeder is used the braid should connect to the *lower* half of the antenna to help feed balance.

The performance of a sloping dipole is quite different from one of the horizontal variety and it can be good for long distance work. The radiation from a sloping dipole shows slant polarisation with both vertical and horizontal components according to the amount of slope. Its lower angle of radiation to the horizon can result in useful low angle gain over a horizontal dipole. Some claim this gain may lie between 3 and 6dB but others give lower figures. Whatever the exact level of gain, it compares favourably with some of the cheaper multi-element trapped beams which may have a performance on their lowest frequency band inferior to that of a dipole. This kind of gain is difficult to realise on the low bands in other ways, and for most amateurs multi-element Yagi beams are out of the question.

There is some high-angled radiation from the sides of the sloping dipole but very little radiation from its high end. An actual plan of the horizontal radiation pattern resembles a heart with a null between its two upper lobes. This null corresponds with the high end of the sloping dipole. A disadvantage is of course that long-distance working will only be possible towards one direction, but this may be overcome by having a group of three or four 'slopers' suspended from a common central support, each with its individual feed line which may be selectively switched to the transmitter or receiver.

There are designs which involve the unused dipoles in such arrangements as reflectors to improve forward gain and front to back ratios, but their construction and adjustment can be complicated and they lie outside the scope of these pages.

Slopers are ideal in many applications where a single support is available. Many people who have beams and towers, mount a sloper on the tower for one of the lower frequency bands, ensuring that the direction of maximum radiation is arranged towards the areas of the globe they want to contact, sometimes having two or more around the tower.

VERTICAL DIPOLES

A vertical half-wave dipole will radiate vertically polarised signals all round, and much of the radiation will be at the low angles favourable for DX working. Unfortunately the centre of this antenna must be at least 0.45-wavelength above the ground if a feed impedance of around 70Ω is needed. Instead it is usually more convenient to arrange for a vertical quarter-wave antenna to be used which can then have its feed point at or near ground level.

Vertical half-waves are not often used by amateurs, although they become practical on the 28MHz band and then can be suspended from existing wires or support cords. A vertical dipole must have its feeder coming away from the radiator wire at right angles if the radiation pattern is to be preserved, and this may present some problems. They cannot be hung down from metal masts or towers either, so their applications are rather restricted. Experiments by John Heys, G3BDQ, using suspended vertical dipoles on 21 and 28MHz showed that vertical quarter-wave radiators using ground planes were more effective.

INVERTED-V DIPOLES

The maximum radiation from any antenna is from the points of high RF current, and a half-wave dipole has this maximum at its centre and for a few feet on either side of the feeder connections. Therefore it is best to make the centre of the dipole as high as possible. If it is only possible to have one high support, an inverted-V arrangement is obviously ideal. In this way it is possible to use one fairly high mast in the centre of a garden or plot in locations where the erection of a pair of similar supports with their attendant guy wires would be difficult. A roof-mounted or chimney-mounted mast may also serve as the centre support for a 'V', and the two ends of the dipole can then drop down on either side of a house or bungalow roof. Such chimney mounting will allow the feeder to be dropped to the shack quite easily if it is located in the house.

Although an inverted-V has its greatest degree of radiation at right angles to the axis of the antenna, its radiation pattern is more omni-directional than that of a horizontal dipole as a result of the fact that the legs are angled downwards.

The inverted-V has an excellent reputation for DX communication on the lower-frequency amateur bands where the erection of large verticals or high horizontal dipoles is not practicable. There are, however, some design features concerning this antenna which must be considered when contemplating making one.

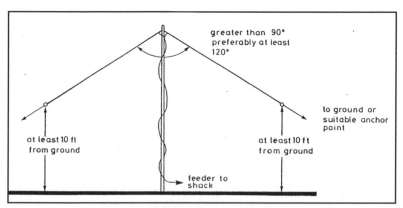

greater than 90°
preferably at least
120°

to ground or
suitable anchor
point

at least 10 ft
from ground

at least 10 ft
from ground

feeder to
shack

The angle between the sloping wires must be at least 90° and preferably 120° or more, as shown in **Fig 3.17**. This angle dictates the centre support height as well as the length of ground needed to accommodate the antenna. For example, when designed for the 3.5MHz band an inverted-V will need a centre support at least 14m (45ft) high and a garden length of around 34m (110ft). By

Fig 3.17 A half-wave inverted-V dipole with the angle between the top wires at 120°. This angle must never fall below 90°. The centre support mast puts the high RF current section of the antenna at the highest point and also carries the weight of the antenna and the feeder. The inverted-V is good for DX working and will give good results on the 3.5MHz band when the mast is only about 14m (45f) high.

contrast, a horizontal dipole needs at least 40m of garden and that neglects to take into account guys to the rear of the end support masts. Again, the inverted-V is ideal for portable operation because one for operation on 20m (14MHz) only needs a lightweight 5m (15ft) pole to hold up its centre.

The sloping of the dipole wires causes a reduction of the resonant frequency for a given dipole length, so about 5% must be subtracted from standard dipole dimensions. One reason for this is the increased self-capacitance of the antenna when its ends are brought closer together and also towards the ground. The self-inductance of the wire is also increased, for the inverted-V approximates to almost a half-turn loop. The calculated wire lengths for inverted-V dipoles on the amateur bands are given in **Table 3.3**.

Frequency	Length	
(kHz)	(ft)	(m)
3600	123' 6"	37.74
7050	63' 1"	19.27
10,100	44' 0"	13.45
14,200	31' 4"	9.57
18,100	24' 7"	7.69
21,200	20' 11"	6.41
24,940	17' 10"	5.45
28,200	15' 9"	4.82
29,200	15' 3"	4.65

Table 3.3 Suggested lengths for inverted-V dipoles.

A further consequence arising from sloping the dipole wires is a change in its radiation resistance. The centre feed impedance falls from the nominal 75Ω of a horizontal dipole to just 50Ω. This of course is ideal for matching the antenna to standard 50Ω impedance coaxial cable. An inverted-V antenna has a higher Q than a simple dipole so it tends to have a narrower bandwidth.

It is not recommended that the ends of an inverted-V are allowed closer to the ground than about 3m (10ft), even on the higher-frequency bands, because there can be a possible danger to people and especially children or animals touching the wire ends which will be at a high RF potential when energised. The effects, although not likely to prove lethal, nevertheless could result in a nasty shock or RF burn, and it seems unlikely that an insurance company would look kindly at any claims resulting from such an accident.

Coaxial feed is recommended with an inverted-V, and the low-loss heavier varieties of cable can be used to advantage, for there are no sag problems when the feeder is fastened up at the top and also down the length of the mast. The feeder will impose no strain upon the antenna or the soldered connections at its feed point. As with an ordinary horizontal dipole, a balun may be used, although they may operate satisfactorily without one.

MULTIBAND DIPOLES

All the dipoles discussed so far have been mono-band antennas. However, it is possible to enable these antennas to operate on several bands using a number of different techniques. This saves having to run several feeders from outside into the shack, means that switching arrangements do not have to be installed.

One of the simplest methods is to remember that a half-wave dipole resonant on one frequency will also resonate at three times this frequency, where it becomes a three half-waves dipole This concept can be conveniently used where a 7MHz half-wave dipole is needed as it will also resonate as a three half-wavelength dipole on 21MHz.

Another technique is to feed several dipoles resonant on different frequencies from the same feeder. Each will present a feed impedance of around 65Ω at its own particular resonant frequency. On all other frequencies its impedance will rise, and it will not accept power from the feeder, and will therefore not affect the performance of the resonant dipole.

For example, a dipole cut for 7MHz will have a normal and low centre impedance on that frequency but, should a second dipole which has been cut for 14MHz also be connected to a common feed point, this second and shorter dipole will not present a centre impedance able to accept power at the lower frequency of 7MHz. The converse will apply when the 14MHz dipole is driven, for then the 7MHz dipole will become a centre-fed full-wave antenna and its high centre impedance will not affect the working of the shorter 14MHz wire.

When using this technique, remember that there is no need to include a dipole for a band where one has already been included at a third of its frequency, ie if a 7MHz element is present then there is no need for one at 21MHz.

A multi-band antenna using a number of horizontal dipoles can be devised in the way suggested, but the extra weight over that of a single dipole will cause considerable sag and a fall in the effective height of all the dipoles. However, it is possible to make an effective multi-band system using the inverted-V configuration with its central high point where the feeder and the combined weight of the dipole wires may be anchored.

Should more than two or three dipoles be used as a multi-band inverted-V, their wire ends must come down to separate anchor points and this makes a rather untidy centre arrangement. A more elegant solution which will allow the construction of a lightweight, five-band inverted-V, and which has single tie points at each end and a common angle at the antenna top, involves the use of flat multi-way ribbon cable for the radiators.

One easily available type of this cable is 10-way, and each of its conductors is made from 14 x 0.13mm tinned copper strands. This cable is 13mm wide and only 1.3mm thick. Each conductor wire is rated at 1.4A continuous current, which means that if used as a half-wave antenna it could handle almost 140W of RF power. The short duty cycles of CW (50%) and SSB operation would enable such a conductor wire to cope quite easily with powers of 100 watts or maybe a little more.

The cable can be obtained in complete lengths of up to 50 metres, and a five-band inverted-V using about 40 metres could be made up from one such piece. This antenna would operate on 3.5, 7, 14, 21 and 28MHz. Using Table 3.3 to find the individual dipole lengths, parts of the cable can be cut away so that the ribbon becomes progressively narrower and lighter towards its ends; each section left being a quarter-wave for the separate bands (leaving out a dipole for 21MHz for the reasons already given). As the ribbon has 10 conductor wires its adjacent pairs can be paralleled at each end, so doubling the power handling capability and in addition broadening the bandwidth by lowering the Q of each dipole. The ribbon inverted-V is shown in **Fig 3.18** (not to scale).

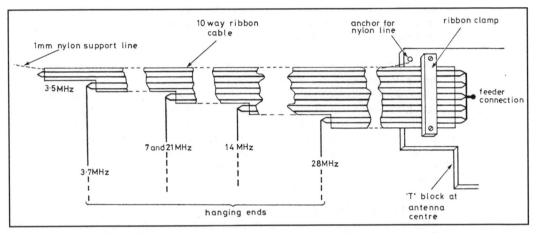

Fig 3.18 A simplified diagram showing how a 10-way cable may be used to construct an effective five-band inverted-V antenna. The thin nylon line used to support the ribbon is 'stitched' along the length of the antenna. By letting the ends of the dipole sections hang down for a few feet, capacitive and other interaction between them is minimised. There is no need to drop the ends of the 3.5MHz dipole. This drawing is not to scale.

If this suggested form of construction is used for the antenna the usual method of end-tying to insulators or a nylon cord will not suffice, for then too much strain will be put on to the longest dipole in the group. It will have to carry its own and also the weight of the other three dipoles, and is likely to break when stressed. One method used to overcome this is to buy a 50m length of thin (1mm diameter) but strong nylon cord, put one end of this through the eye of a stout packing needle and 'stitch' it along the multi-way ribbon cable. The stitches can be quite large, each one being around half a metre long, and the end product will be a strong and lightweight multi-dipole top which can be easily supported by a normal 12 to 14m (40 to 45ft) pole or mast. The ends can be secured by the thin nylon cord so that the top angle is the recommended 120° or so.

The ends of half-wave dipoles are at quite high RF voltages, and their proximity to other wires etc will capacitively detune them. It is therefore expedient to allow a few feet of the 7, 14 and 28MHz dipole ends to dangle freely away from the remaining ribbon. A good centre connecting block of Perspex or similar material will make a suitable anchor point for the ribbon ends and also the feeder (Fig 3.15). The ends of the longest dipole sections must not come right down to ground level but should be arranged to terminate at about 3m (10ft) above the ground as before.

Simpler versions of the antenna for use on just two or three bands may be constructed by using 300Ω ribbon feeder instead of the 10-way cable. Another constructional method involves the use of individual dipole wires bound together at about 1m (3ft) intervals. It takes longer to make up such an antenna from individual wires and the end product is not so neat or clean looking.

If operation on the 3.5MHz band is not required the multi-band antenna can be made much smaller. In turn the resulting geometry means that a much smaller mast can be used. One only about 8m (25ft) is needed in this case, simplifying the construction of the support considerably.

Although the spurious signal rejection of modern rigs is normally very good, when using a multi-band antenna such as the one described it is always advisable to use an ATU. Not only will this ensure a good match for the transmitter at all times, but it will also provide an additional tuned circuit in the feed line. This will not only attenuate any unwanted transmitter signals, but it will also reduce incoming signals on bands other than the one being used. This could prevent the receiver front end being overloaded; especially of there are very strong signals on other bands.

GI4JTF MULTIPLE PARALLEL DIPOLES

Another design for a multiple dipole system was developed by E Squance, GI4JTF, and appeared in the March 1982 issue of *RadCom*. The design shows that the lengths that would be expected from the straight dipole length formula are not exactly correct and need to be shortened as a result of the interaction between the different elements of the antenna for the different bands. The lengths are given in **Table 3.4**.

Resonant frequency (kHz)	Length of dipole metres (feet)
7050	20.57 (67.5)
14,250	10.31 (33.82)
28,775	5.08 (16.67)

Table 3.4: Lengths for GI4JTF multiple dipole system.

The antenna is fed with 75Ω flat twin feeder which is taken back to an ATU. The antenna wire used was multi-stranded 2 mm copper wire which was spaced every 660mm (2ft) using old felt tip pen bodies that were cut and drilled. Overall details of the construction and layout of the antenna are shown in **Fig 3.19** and

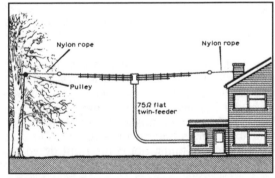

Fig 3.19 Overall layout of the GI4JTF multiple HF dipole.

the attachment of the feeder wires and spacers is shown in **Fig 3.20**.

The centre of the dipole consisted of a polythene plate measuring 110 x 70 x 5mm (4.5 x 2.75 x 0.19in) and is shown in **Fig 3.21**. Two strips of copper measuring 63 x 12.7mm (2.5 x 0.5inch) were bolted to the plate, one either side to prevent the pull of the wires pulling the bolts through the polythene. The wires were then fed through the centre of the dipole centre plate for rigidity and soldered to copper strip. The feeder was passed through the plate from front to back to prevent whipping when in use. The whole assembly was then liberally coated in marine varnish before being hoisted to the working height.

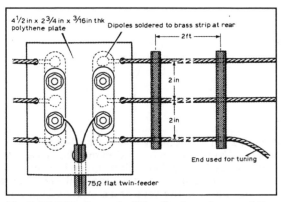

Fig 3.20 Attachment of the feeder wires and the

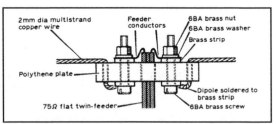

Fig 3.21 End view of the centre plate showing the mechanical details.

LOADED DIPOLES

Not everyone has room for a full-sized dipole. Although those for the higher frequency bands are smaller, even these can be difficult to fit into some locations. Also, by their very nature, those antennas for the low bands are very much larger and need large plots if full-sized antennas are to be installed. Fortunately it is possible to reduce the physical length of many antennas. This can be achieved with only a small degradation to the performance of the antenna. The reason for this is that the middle section of a dipole radiates most of the power. In fact, 71% of the total radiation occurs from the central half of a dipole's length.

One method is to bend the legs of the antenna, thereby enabling it to fit into a small plot. The ends can be dropped down to ensure that the centre remains as high as possible, or the antenna can be arranged in a form of zig-zag fashion. This can often work reasonably well.

Another alternative is to use inductive loading in each dipole leg. Using this approach it is possible to achieve resonance and have little loss with a dipole only half the normal length for the frequency used. Off-centre loading can be achieved by inserting an inductor at pre-determined position along each of the dipole legs. However, there are several considerations to be noted when deciding which is the most useful point for the loading coils.

The greater the distance they are from the antenna centre the more efficient the system will be but, when that distance is increased, larger values of inductance are needed. An increase in inductance results in an increase in the resistive loss, a narrower antenna bandwidth, and a heavy coil. The coil adds weight to the antenna increasing the strain, and degree of droop at the centre. If a dipole is halved in length (ie the top is only a

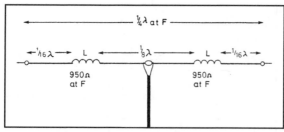

Fig 3.22 An inductively loaded half-size dipole. The lengths of each wire section may be calculated from the half-wave dimensions given in Table 3.1. The radiation pattern of a normal full-size dipole will also apply in the case of a shortened version, but its efficiency will be reduced. Coils made from very thick wire or tube, and wound on a high-grade former, will increase the efficiency by reducing resistive and other losses.

Band	Inductance	Frequency when tuned with 100pF in parallel
(MHz)	(µH)	(MHz)
3.6	40	2.6
7.0	25	3.2
14.0	12	4.5
21.0	8	5.6
28.0	6	6.6

Table 3.5 Loading inductors for half-wave dipoles.

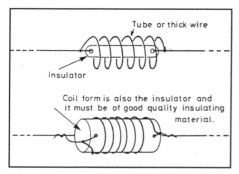

Fig 3.23 Two ways to insert the loading coils along the dipole wires. Self-supporting inductors can easily be adjusted by squeezing the turns together or apart. The loading coils can be set to the correct inductance before they are used in the antenna, and any final trimming to resonance will only involve the length of the end wires.

quarter-wavelength long overall) and a loading inductance is put at the half-way joint along each shortened leg, the inductors required must each have a reactance of approximately 950Ω at the operating frequency (see **Fig 3.22**).

By using this information it is possible to determine the actual inductance needed on each amateur band. **Table 3.5** gives these inductance values. It also gives the resonant frequency of the inductor when it is placed in parallel with a 100pF capacitor for testing and adjustment purpose. Winding coils to a specific inductance is not an easy task for amateurs because there are so many variables to consider: coil diameter, turns per inch, wire thickness and the coil length to diameter ratio. The coils must either be wound on a high-grade insulating material or be stout enough to be self-supporting using thick wire or tubing (**Fig 3.23**). By adding the parallel capacitor when testing and adjusting the coil it is relatively easy to determine the inductance. The coils can be trimmed with some accuracy. This can be done by squeezing or opening out the turns of the self-supporting types, or removing or adding turns to those coils which are wound on formers. It is suggested that a dip oscillator coupled to a frequency counter be used when adjusting the coils. This is done without any kind of connection to the antenna wires.

An insulator can be inserted half-way along each of the short dipole legs, and the coils (without the 100pF capacitors) may be soldered into place across them (Fig 3.22). Those coils wound on formers can be fully weather proofed by giving them a liberal coating of silicone-rubber sealant. Insulation problems are not great, because the RF voltages will be low where the coils are positioned along the wires at their half-way points.

The finished loaded short dipole may not resonate at exactly the desired frequency at first test, so some adjustments can be made to the lengths of the dipole end sections. A dip oscillator / frequency counter arrangement can be coupled to a single-turn link across the dipole centre (the antenna may be lowered to about 3m (10ft) above ground to do this, or instead a check on the SWR should be made as the transmitted frequency is moved across the band. The lowest SWR normally indicates antenna resonance. An antenna RF noise bridge can also be used to check for dipole resonance when used in conjunction with a receiver.

Even a properly resonated, loaded half-size dipole will not be as effective as a full-sized antenna, but it will still prove to be a very useful radiator and show the same directional characteristics. The shortened dipole must not be confused with a trap dipole, a type which is little shorter than a normal half-wave on the lowest band covered. Trapped systems are used to allow multi-band operation from one antenna using a single feeder and they are not easy to make and set up correctly.

Loaded Dipole for 40 and 80m

This design by Vince Lear, G3TKN / ZL1VL, appeared in the October 2004 issue of *RadCom*. In this design the antenna uses loading coils in place of more conventional traps to obtain two-band operation. The idea of using loading coils in this way was described over 40 years ago in an article entitled 'Multi-band Antenna Using Loading Coils' by W J Lattin, W4JRW, that appeared in the April 1961 issue of *QST*. The concept offers the advantage of simplicity over trap construction, and also results in considerable shortening of the antenna, which now takes up less space than the popular G5RV with its 31.09m (102ft) top, and the standard 33.53m (110ft) trap dipole.

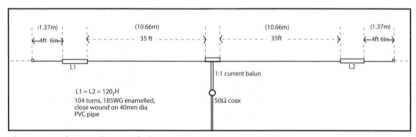

L1 = L2 = 120μH
104 turns, 185WG enamelled,
close wound on 40mm dia
PVC pipe

1:1 current balun

50Ω coax

Fig 3.24 Dimensions of the 80 / 40 metre dipole.

The inductive reactance of a coil increases as the frequency applied to it increases. In the 40 / 80 metre loaded dipole (**Fig 3.24**), the coils are sufficiently large that they show a high impedance on 40m, and provide inductive loading on 80m. Lattin found that values between 80μH to 120μH gave good results when used in this way, the larger values of inductance requiring less wire on the outer sections for 80m resonance. However, Lattin acknowledged that no exact formulae have been found to determine the relationship between coil size, wire lengths, and the two frequencies for dual-band resonance. Therefore, the published design may be regarded as a starting point for experimentation.

It should be appreciated that when an antenna is inductively loaded several things happen. The most noticeable is the reduction in bandwidth of the system. The greater the loading, the smaller the bandwidth. The efficiency of the antenna also decreases. However, this decrease in efficiency is dependent on where in the aerial the loading coils are placed and, more importantly, on the construction of the loading coils. In a loaded wire aerial, the size and weight of the loading coils have to be important considerations, so to some extent there will always be some compromise between efficiency and what is practical.

As the loading is increased and the aerial becomes shorter, the feed point impedance decreases. With a very heavily-loaded antenna, it may not be possible to feed it with 50Ω coax, and some extra matching circuitry may need to be employed.

Using loading coils to achieve two-band resonance does mean that one has no choice but to place the coils a quarter-wavelength out either side of the feed-point on the higher frequency. The advantage is that, on 80m, the radiation resistance is kept at a higher level in this configuration than if the coils were placed close-in to the feed-point.

The disadvantage is that it results in a narrower operating bandwidth when the aerial is used on 80m. A good match is obtained to a 50Ω feeder on both 40m and 80m, although the bandwidth on 80m is restricted to about 60kHz between the 2:1 SWR points. No such problem occurs on 40m, where an SWR of about 1.5:1 was achieved across most of the band.

In this antenna the 120μH coils were constructed by close-winding 104 turns of 1.25mm (18SWG) enamelled copper wire on to a 17.8cm (7in) length of white PVC pipe of 40mm (1.6in) diameter. The winding length was 14cm (5.5in). Note that the total length of wire needed to construct these coils is a little more than that available from a standard 250g reel of wire. A 1kg reel of wire was used for the design antenna (available from Scientific Wire Company, 18 Raven Rd, South Woodford, London E18 1HW,UK; tel: +44(0)20 8505 0002, website www.wires.co.uk). An alternative, although this has not been tried, could be to divide the wire from a 250g reel into two equal lengths and use these to wind as many turns as possible on to the two formers, making sure that they have the same number of turns.

Fig 3.25 The coil used in the 40 / 80 metre dipole is made from standard 40 mm (1.6 inch) diameter PVC pipe. It is 17.8 cm (7inch) long, with a winding length of 14 cm (5.5 in). Holes are drilled at each end to secure the aerial wire.

With care, it should be possible to achieve about 92 close-wound turns which will yield around 106μH. The dimensions of the antenna will be affected, but those given for the 120μH version should make a good starting point for experimentation.

As always, when experimenting with antennas, make them longer than expected and then trim down for resonance. The PVC piping is obtainable from most DIY outlets in 1.8m (6ft) lengths.

The antenna wire was fixed to each end of the loading coil via holes drilled in the PVC pipe. The ends of the coil were anchored through small holes in the coil, and soldered to the aerial wire.

A short section of the PVC piping was checked out in a microwave oven to examine for any heating effect. None was found, so it was therefore assumed that the material was quite suitable for use in this application. Care should be exercised in the use of some PVC piping which may be quite lossy if it is carbon-filled. The whole coil assembly was given two coats of marine yacht varnish. The operation of the antenna was not affected during periods of heavy rain, so the weather proofing provided by the varnish appeared quite adequate.

The antenna handled 400W from a linear amplifier without any problems, although this was only done where the SWR was no greater than 1.5:1. The photos (**Fig 3.25** and **Fig 3.26**) show the coil construction and the aerial components, together with a commercial Ferromagnetics current-mode balun (Ferromagnetics, PO Box 577, Mold, Flintshire CH7 1AH, UK; website: www.ferromagnetics.co.uk). Losses are greater in a voltage mode balun if used off resonance where reactive components are present. A current-mode balun can easily be constructed by winding 5 to 8 turns of RG58 coax (5mm diameter) around a pair of stacked ferrite rings.

The 40m section needed to be 10.66m (35ft) per leg as opposed to 10.05m (33ft) for resonance. This was the same length as found by W4JRW. If an antenna has end capacity-loading (as would be the case for

Fig 3.26 The 40 / 80m loaded dipole uses a commercial Ferromagnetics current-mode balun at its feed-point (see text). The antenna is made from flexible grey plastic-covered 14 strand copper wire.

a top-loaded vertical with a large capacity hat of wires fanning out from its top), its length can be reduced due to the end capacity. However, in the case of the 40m section in the 40 / 80m loaded dipole, inductive loading is seen at the end, and hence the opposite occurs with a resulting increase required for resonance at 7MHz. This effect should not be confused with inductive loading in series with an aerial rather than at its end. In the former case, the aerial will be electrically lengthened, and hence a shorter length of wire will be required for resonance.

The trimming of the end sections is very critical. It was found that 1.27m (4ft 2in) gave resonance on 3774kHz with a resulting 1:1 SWR, the 2:1 SWR points occurring at 3805kHz and 3742kHz. The antenna should, of course, be trimmed for one's favourite part of the band. The use of the auto ATU allowed for some limited excursion outside of the 2:1 SWR points on 80m. However, it should be appreciated that this in no way reduces mismatched line loss on the coaxial feeder.

As the coils also offer a high impedance on 15m, the inner section can be used as a near $3\lambda / 2$ dipole on that band. The actual resonance in this mode was found to be 20.2MHz but, using an ATU it was able to deliver full power across all of the 15m band on this design.

The antenna may be used on 160m instead of 80m by extending the wires on the outside of the loading coils from around 1.22m (4ft) to 7.62m (25ft). This gave a 1:1 SWR on 1840kHz. The bandwidth between the 2:1 SWR points is in the region of 35kHz on 160m. The antenna will now function on 40 and 160m.

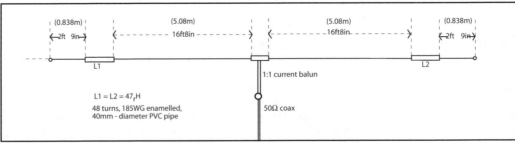

Fig 3.27 The 20 / 40m loaded dipole.

A very successful 20 / 40m version was also constructed (**Fig 3.27**) using the same principles as used for 40 and 80m. This had an overall length of 11.89m (39f) and used coils of 47µH. The coils were again made of 1.25mm (18SWG) enamelled copper wire, close-wound with 48 turns on standard 40mm (1.6in) diameter PVC pipe. Coil formers of 10cm (4in) length were used. The aerial had 5.08m (16ft 8in) inner sections with 0.83metre (2ft 9in) outer ends.

The SWR on 20m was less than 1.5:1 across most of the band, and the antenna showed a 1:1 SWR on 7072kHz with a 2:1 SWR bandwidth of 96kHz. Typical dipole performance resulted on 20m, with good all-round reports on 7MHz.

If the standard 40 / 80m design is fed with open-wire line (or 450Ω ladder-line) coupled into the transceiver via a balanced ATU, the antenna could be operated efficiently on both 17m and 20m. The inner section will operate as two half-waves in phase on 20m, and as a double extended Zepp on 17m with theoretical broadside gain figures of 1.6dBd and 3dBd, respectively. On 21MHz and above, a multi-lobe pattern will result.

SHORTENED DIPOLE FOR 3.5MHz
The idea of reducing the size of an antenna is of importance to most people, so another option is mentioned here. This idea for a 3.5MHz dipole (**Fig 3.28**) was mentioned in 'Technical Topics' (*RadCom* November 1971), and was originally covered in *DL-QTC* (No 5 1971).

In his design DL7LJ uses an inverted-V arrangement and two coils, one in each leg of the dipole. These consist of 145 turns of aluminium wire (chosen for its low weight) 1.5mm diameter wound on a 22mm diameter former over a length of 350mm. With 0.6m between the centre and the inductor and a further 6.55m of radiating wire, this gives a total length of 7.5m for each leg, and this provides a considerable saving in space.

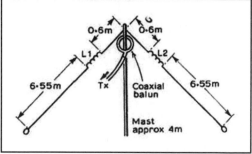

Fig 3.28 The DL7LJ short dipole for 3.5MHz.

The SWR curves indicate that the resonance is fairly sharp, as would be expected for a shortened antenna, although it should be possible to cover at least 100kHz.

MULTI-BAND TRAP DIPOLE

Over the years a number of designs have appeared for multi-band trap dipoles covering 80, 40, 20, 15 and 10 metres. One commercially available version was the G8KW which was fed with 75Ω coax. Another similar design is shown here (**Fig 3.29**), although this one is fed with 50Ω coax and is in an inverted-V format.

Each leg of the antenna consists of two lengths of wire, the one closest to the centre is 32ft 6in long, whereas the outer section is 21ft 6in. The traps comprise 23 turns of 18SWG wire on a 30mm (1.25in) diameter former with a winding length of approximately 65mm (2.5in). The capacitor is 50pF and must be a high voltage type to withstand the antenna end voltage when used with a transmitter. Before connecting the trap to the antenna it is made resonant at 7.1MHz.

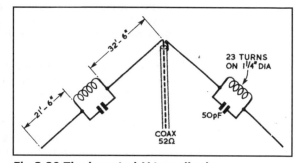

Fig 3.29 The inverted-V trap dipole.

The antenna forms a half-wave on 80m. On 40m it uses the trap and similarly is a half-wave antenna. On the higher frequency bands it acts as a multiple half-wave antenna, and as expected there are sharp lobes. Nevertheless it makes a very useful multi-band dipole.

THE TERMINATED TILTED FOLDED DIPOLE

The original design for this antenna, often referred to as the T2FD in view of the letters of its name, was published by G L Countryman. The design covers a frequency range of 7 - 35MHz and it is only a third of a wavelength at the lowest frequency of operation. It is the ease of installation of this antenna combined with the fact that it is broadband, relatively compact and only requires one high support that has made it very popular, particularly for listening applications.

Fig 3.30 shows the principal features of the T2FD. It bears a superficial resemblance to an ordinary folded dipole, but its dimensions, the use of

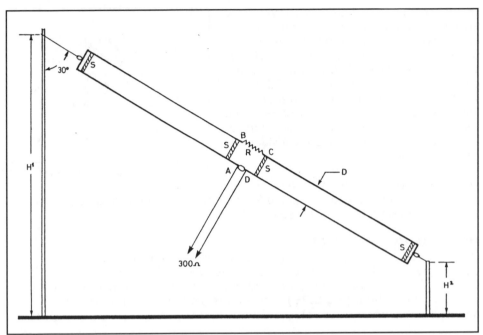

Fig 3.30 The T2FD antenna. The version of the antenna shown is designed for operation down to 7MHz. The high support H1 need only be 10.7m (35ft) high and the lower support H2 need only be 2m (6ft).

a non-inductive terminating resistor R, and the 20 to 40° tilt result in an aperiodic or non-resonant vertically-polarised radiator which has a useful frequency ratio of at least 4:1.

A T2FD designed for 7MHz will work satisfactorily on all frequencies up to 30MHz, to a lesser degree even on half its design frequency (3.5MHz), and can be easily fed with 300Ω impedance untuned line.

When set up at its optimum slope angle of 30°, the T2FD displays an almost omni-directional, low-angle radiation pattern similar to that of a quarter-wave vertical or Marconi antenna. There is, however, some reduction in field strength at the high end of the antenna, and this must be kept in mind when considering its erection and use.

The antenna is useful in cramped locations, for on its design frequency it is somewhat shorter than an equivalent half-wave antenna. On 7MHz a half-wave is about 20m (66ft) long from end to end but a T2FD will only be about 14.33m (47ft) in length. Also, the T2FD only needs a single support 11m (36ft) high and an additional short 1.8m (6ft) pole at its low end.

There are some rigid design parameters to consider when a T2FD is assembled. The length of each leg (when measuring from the centre of the wires across the end spreaders to the feed point or the terminating resistor) should be 50,000 / f (kHz) metres (50,000 / f (kHz) x 3.28 feet). The total top length and the lengths AS and CD in Fig 3.30 will be twice this calculated length. The frequency is the lowest operating frequency of the antenna although, as has been mentioned, a T2FD will work with reduced efficiency at half this frequency. The spacing between the two radiator wires D in metres can be found by dividing 3000 by the frequency in kilohertz.

The terminating resistor must be non-inductive for the antenna to operate satisfactorily. If an inductive resistor is used the antenna resonates on some frequencies and then the feeder must then be used as a tuned line, and the flat 300Ω impedance at the feed point is lost.

The terminating resistor value is to some extent determined by the impedance of the feed line used. When using 300Ω twin lead to feed the antenna, the optimum resistor value is about 400Ω, although any resistance value between 375 and 425Ω will work well. With 450Ω open wire feed line a 500Ω resistor is satisfactory, and the use of 600Ω line requires a 650Ω resistor.

Some experimenters have fed the T2FD antenna with low-impedance line (including coaxial cable), but then the terminating resistor value becomes very critical and must be within 5Ω of optimum. The terminating resistor must dissipate about 35% of the transmitter output power. This may seem to be a serious power loss, but in fact it only represents a signal loss of from 1.5 to 2dB (below half an S-point) which is more than compensated for by the low angle of radiation from the antenna.

A T2FD antenna can be assembled by using two wires of equal length, each wire making up one of the sections AB and CD as shown in the diagram. Their lengths for each band are given in **Table 3.6** where the spacing distances D are

Band(MHz)	Length AB and CD (also top length)	Spacing D
1.8	55.54m (182' 2")	1.66m (5' 5")
3.6	27.76m (91' 1")	0.83m (2' 8")
7	14.28m (46' 10")	0.42m (1' 5")
10.1	9.9m (32' 6")	0.3m (1' 0")
14.15	7.06m (23' 2")	0.21m (0' 8")
21.2	4.7m (15' 6")	0.14m (0' 5")
29	3.44m (11' 4")	0.1m (0' 4")

Table 3.6 Terminated tilted folded dipoles.

also shown. The heights of the antenna supports on different bands have not been calculated, but the mast height of 11m (36ft) for a T2FD designed for the 7MHz band may of course be interpolated to discover the heights needed on other bands.

Trees or buildings can also be used as end supports, but when buildings are used there will be some additional attenuation of the radiation from that end of the antenna. A 2m (6ft) anchor point at the low end of the antenna can be used for all antenna lengths, its main purpose being to safeguard the wires from the attentions of animals or children.

It has been found that when the antenna is pulled tight, it only needs a centre spreader and a spreader at each end. However, there is no reason

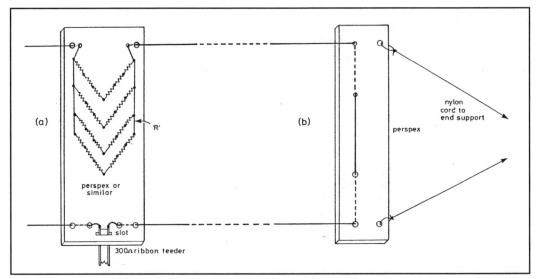

Fig 3.31 (a) The centre block of a T2FD, which accommodates a chain of non-inductive resistors, provides a connection point for the 300Ω ribbon feeder and also is an antenna spreader. (b) How the antenna wire is threaded through holes in the two end spreaders. Perspex strips 6mm (1/4in) thick are suitable as spreaders. For a 7MHz version *of* the T2FD only two end and one centre spreaders are needed.

why additional spreaders cannot be used towards the centre of each leg of the antenna. If the end spreaders are fashioned from a material like Perspex sheet, the antenna wires can then be threaded through as shown and no additional antenna insulators will be needed.

The antenna centre block has on it the connections to the 300Ω feeder and also the terminating resistor. The latter is made up from a series-parallel arrangement of low-wattage types. The 50% duty cycle of CW (Morse) or the even shorter duty cycle of SSB telephony will determine the wattage needed in the resistor chain. Of course, a continuous carrier is needed for certain other transmissions, such as FSK or FM, and this must be borne in mind when determining the terminating resistor power dissipation. The resistor will only dissipate about 18W on CW with a power output of 100W, and this will be even less on the SSB mode.

It is suggested that 24 resistors, each with a resistance value of 270Ω and a power rating of 2 watts, will be more than adequate. The resistors will be well within their ratings under key-down conditions, and on SSB a peak power of 300 watts can be used.

The resistors are wired into four lines, each of which has six in series (1620Ω per line), and these four lines when paralleled will produce a final resistance value of 405Ω. The resistors must be of the carbon-film type. Weatherproofing this assembly is necessary, and may be done as described before.

If a single high-wattage resistor is used, a suggested method of connection is shown in **Fig 3.32**.

A correctly designed T2FD using a non-inductive terminating resistor presents a uniform feed impedance right across its frequency range. The antenna described should have a 300Ω feeder which may be taken right to the shack and the station ATU. As an alternative when long feeder runs are used that may run through the house or near other objects, the feeder may

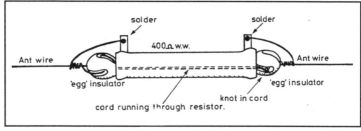

Fig 3.32 The way to connect a single high-wattage resistor to the centre of a T2FD antenna. The cord running through the centre of the resistor takes the strain away from the connections. A thermoplastic cord must not be used in this position, and all electrical connections should be waterproofed.

be connected to a 4:1 balun which will bring down the impedance to 75Ω (unbalanced) and allow the use of coaxial cable.

One disadvantage of any aperiodic antenna is that it will radiate any harmonic content of the transmitter output, so it is advisable that an additional tuned circuit in the form of an ATU is always used.

Experience of a number of people who have used the T2FD indicates that although the antenna is balanced and is not fed against earth, it seems to operate more effectively when they are positioned over several buried radial wires which connect back to the station ATU. This is not surprising, for the T2FD design seems to have much in common with vertical Marconi antennas which of course rely greatly upon good low resistance earths.

COMBINED GROUNDED TERMINATED DIPOLE
The T2FD has the advantage of being a very convenient antenna arrangement for many stations, but a significant portion of the power is dissipated in the terminating resistor. While it does not significantly degrade the performance of the antenna, it nevertheless does absorb power that could otherwise be radiated and this goes against the grain for many radio hams who rightly believe that it is best to radiate the maximum amount of power. In an attempt to improve the efficiency of the T2FD DK5IQ looked into a method of eliminating the terminating resistor while still retaining its convenience. The idea which appeared in *CQ-DL* 4/99 and later in 'Eurotek' in the August 1999 issue of *RadCom* details a method for achieving this, with the antenna termed a CGFD or Combined Grounded Folded Dipole and shown in **Fig 3.33**.

Starting with a 10MHz folded dipole a 4:1 balun was connected to the feed point and then 50Ωcoax was used to connect it to the equipment in the shack. Next an insulator was inserted in the opposite wire to the balun and across this was connected 7m of 300Ω slotted ribbon feeder which terminates in what was termed a pre-tuning unit near the ground.

The lower end of the ribbon cable can be terminated in a variety of ways. If a 300Ω resistor is used the antenna behaves in the same way as a T2FD, but with the advantage that the terminating resistor does not have to remain up in the air where it adds weight to the antenna. However,

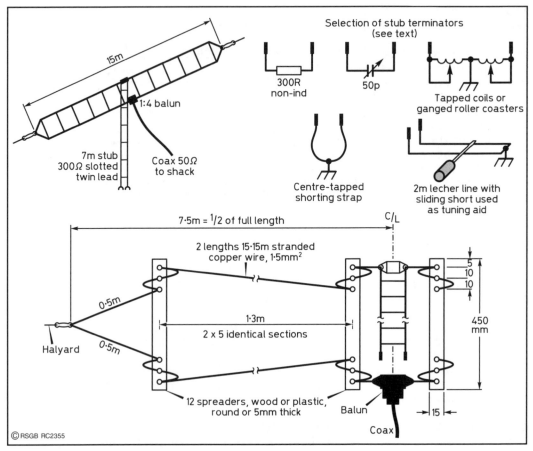

Fig 3.33 DK5IQ CGFD is based on the T2FD but the power dissipating terminating resistor is replaced by a stub which is terminated in a shorted grounded extension, a capacitor or an inductor.

other termination solutions may be added instead which eliminate the power wastage by the resistor.

The first alternative is to extend the stub from 7m to 8.45m and when the end is shorted and earthed, this provides a level of SWR better than 2.5:1 on all bands, and this can be tuned with an ATU. For situations where a lower level of SWR is required the stub may be terminated as follows: with a 5 - 50pF tuning capacitor (spacing commensurate with power) for 10, 14, and 28MHz; shorted with 0.65m wire on 24.9MHz, and a ganged pair of roller coasters on all bands except 14MHz.

If the 7m stub runs into the shack, the coax feed should be kept well separated from it and the best termination can be selected with a manually operated switch. If the stub is terminated remotely then relay selection and motor driven coils and capacitors can be used. As the values are location dependent, some experimentation is necessary. A useful tool for tuning is a 2m length of closely spaced open wire line, which can be shorted using a sliding bar along it while monitoring the level of SWR.

Finally, the CGFD does not need to be angled as the T2FD and can be installed horizontally, vertically or as an inverted-V.

ON9CVD SHORT HORIZONTAL DIPOLE FOR 3.5 AND 14MHz

This design for a shortened horizontal dipole was developed by Bob van Donselaar, ON9CVD, and originally published in *Electron* in July 1999, and later as part of the 'Eurotek' series in the October 1999 issue of *RadCom*.

This design uses capacitive loading to provide shortening of the span required and the possibility of operation on two bands. A given amount of end loading has different effects on different frequencies. By separately varying the length of the radiator and the amount of end loading, an antenna can be set up to resonate and have a low impedance feed point on two frequencies, eg in the 80 and 20m bands.

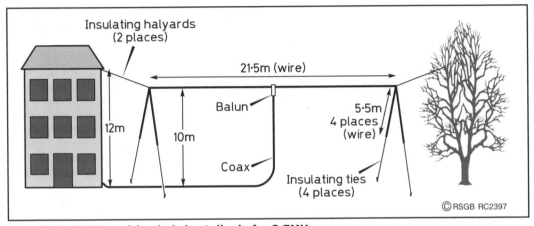

Fig 3.34 ON9CVD end-loaded short dipole for 3.7MHz.

The antenna is shown in **Fig 3.34** and consists of a horizontal dipole, centre-fed by 50Ω coax through a 1:1 balun and end-loaded on each end with two identical inverted-V wires. These loading wires consist of wires at 90° to the dipole wire and to each other.

To check out and optimize the performance, the antenna was modelled using *EZNEC*. The antenna was modelled for the horizontal wire 10m above average earth (ie with a conductance of 5mS / m, and a dielectric constant 13). The wire used was 1.8mm diameter. The design was optimised, and the length was adjusted for resonance at 14.14MHz and the end loading for 3.745MHz. This sequence is also recommended when physically adjusting the antenna in its actual environment. The result is a dipole with a length of 21.5m for the top section, and with end loading wires of 5.5m at 10m above average earth.

To assess the performance on 3.7MHz, the loaded dipole was compared on the computer with that of a full-size (38.5m) dipole and also one shortened to 21.5m by inductive loading with two 19ìH coils having a Q of 200 which were located either side of the feed point. These were all at

	Azimuth @ 0° Gain Elevation (dBi) (°) * *		Azimuth @ 90° Gain Elevation (dBi) (°) * *		At Resonance Impedance (ohms)	SWR ref 50 ohms	Bandwidth (kHz) *
End loaded	5.82	53.2	5.82	38	31.9	1.6	151
Half wave	6.33	57.5	6.33	38	49.2	1.02	202
Coil loaded	4.55	55.5	4.55	38	15.9	3.2	47

Table 3.7 3.7MHz dipole performance comparison. *Gain here is computed with reference to an isotropic radiator, and the elevation is computed as the angle for the lower -3dB point with respect to the maximum radiation. The bandwidth is computed as for a tuned circuit, ie between frequencies where resistance and reactance are equal. It should not be taken as the SWR bandwidth; where the impedance is 50Ω at resonance, the SWR at the bandwidth extremes is approx 2.6:1.

the same height and using the same feed frequency. The feed point impedance, gain, elevation angle and bandwidth from these calculations are displayed in **Table 3.7**.

There is only one lobe to the radiation pattern. This is straight up, as is desirable for short haul working. The gain of -3dB point with respect to the maximum is at 38° above the horizon. In other words there is enough low-angle radiation for some long haul contacts. The gain is only marginally lower than that of the full-length dipole at little more than half the span and well above the gain of the coil-loaded dipole of the same length. The SWR is low enough for many commercial transceivers over much of the phone end of the band. It is somewhat narrower than the full-length dipole but much wider than the coil loaded one.

For operation on 20m the comparison was made with a half-wave dipole 10.4m long and 10m above earth. As the 21.5m long antenna does not have the figure of eight pattern of the half-wave dipole, the gain and elevation angles and plotted in **Fig 3.35**.

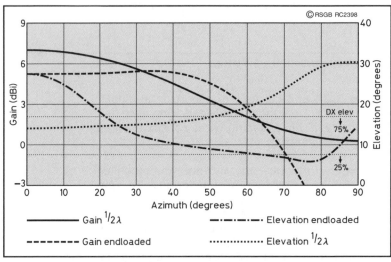

Fig 3.35 14MHz gain and elevation as functions of azimuth (only one quadrant shown). DX elevation, as shown in the plot, refers to the optimum take-off to communicate with a station >1500km away. Observations at the Rohde & Schwartz company have established at which angles above the horizon signals were received and over what percentage of the time. At 3.7MHz, the elevation angles are below 44° 75% of the time, below 38° 25% of the time. At 14MHz, these angles were 17° and 7° respectively.

	Impedance at resonance (ohms)	SWR ref 50 ohms	Bandwidth (kHz)
End loaded	49.8	1.0	362
Half wave	73.1	1.46	140

Table 3.8 Feed point impedance, SWR and bandwidth.

The feed point impedance, SWR and bandwidth are shown in **Table 3.8**. It turns out that the longer antenna is perfectly matched to 50Ω but that the bandwidth is much narrower than that of the half wave dipole, although it is adequate to cover the CW and much of the phone band.

Chapter 4
Tuned Feeder Antennas

One class of antennas that are not as widely used as they might be are tuned feeder antennas. Using an open wire tuned feed line as part of the overall antenna system, they enable multi-band operation to be achieved. This type of antenna may often be referred to as a 'Doublet' or a 'centre fed Zepp'. The latter term is really a contradiction in terms, as a true Zepp is a resonant wire fed at one end. Nevertheless, these tuned feeder antennas are particularly useful because they enable multi-band operation to be achieved, although they do require the use of an ATU to ensure that there is a sufficiently good match to the receiver, or more importantly the transmitter.

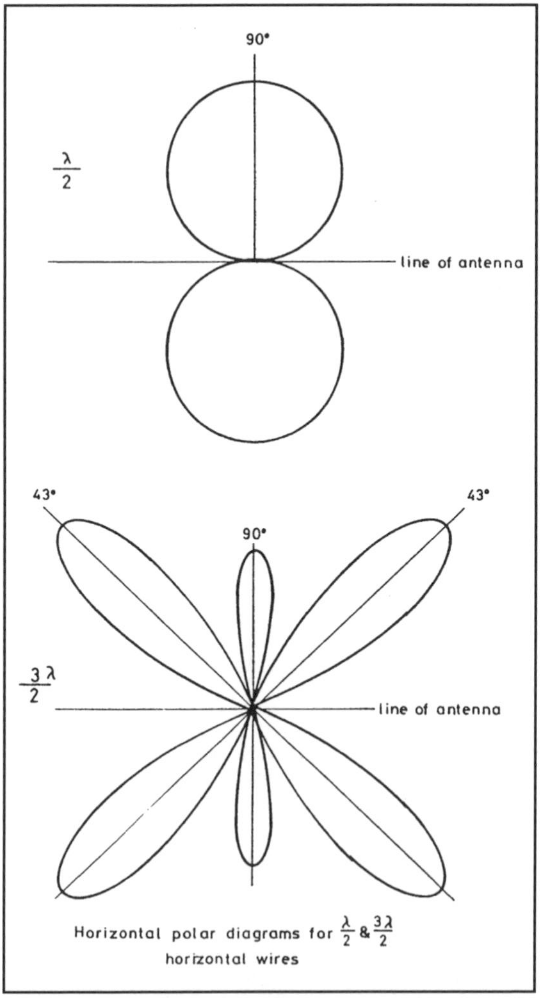

The tuned feed line antennas can be used over a wide range of frequencies. However, as the frequency changes the radiation pattern of the antenna will alter. A half-wavelength antenna has the maximum radiation at right angles to the axis or line of the antenna. As the electrical length of the antenna increases the phasing of the radiation from the antenna wire means that new lobes appear and grow. Examples of polar diagrams of a half-wave and also a three half-wave radiator are shown in **Fig 4.1**.

TUNED FEED LINES

The key to tuned feed line antennas is naturally the feeder. As discussed in Chapter 2, these open-wire feed lines have a characteristic impedance which relates to the diameter of the wire used and the spacing between the feed wires. This impedance is important in many applications but is of no consequence when considering centre-fed antennas which use tuned lines. The antennas discussed in this chapter mostly use tuned feed lines and therefore the impedance of such lines can be disregarded.

Fig 4.1 Horizontal polar diagrams for half-wave and three half-wave horizontal wires.

Tuned feed lines operate on the principle that they are really a part of the antenna and have 'standing waves' along their lengths. Standing waves are a feature of most radiating wires but, if two such wires of equal length are closely spaced (in terms of wavelength) and fed in anti-phase, in theory they will not radiate. In practice they radiate a very small proportion of the RF power applied. A clearer understanding of the action of tuned feeders may be gained from **Fig 4.2**.

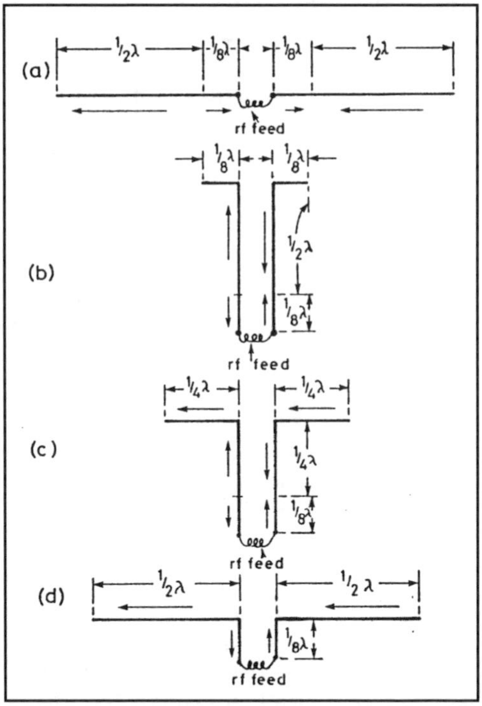

The instantaneous current along a centre-fed antenna when each leg is 5/8-wavelength long is shown in Fig 4.2(a). For simplicity the RF generator connects right at the antenna centre. It will be seen that the currents in the half-wave long ends of the antenna are in phase (they seem to run in the same direction) and that the small currents in the two eighth-wave sections near the centre are in opposition to them. The RF in the smaller centre section will still contribute towards the total radiation from the antenna, but will also have an influence upon its pattern of radiation.

This picture changes dramatically when all but the final eighth-wavelengths at the antenna ends is pulled down and runs in parallel towards the RF source (Fig 4.2(b)). Along the length of the parallel section (really now a feeder) are equal and opposite currents, and therefore this feeder radiates very little. The total radiation is from the truncated and tiny top section where the antenna currents are in phase.

Fig 4.2 Four different doublet antenna arrangements using the same total length of wire for the tops and the feed lines. In each example, the antenna currents along the doublet tops are in phase, while the feeder currents along each leg are anti-phase and will cancel.

The diagram in Fig 4.2(c) shows an intermediate situation which has a full half-wavelength making up the radiating top section, and Fig 4.2(d) illustrates the in-phase currents along a top made from two half-wavelengths. In this diagram the feed line is shown as only one eighth-wavelength long, but it can be of any convenient length without any impairment to the performance of the radiating antenna top.

THE BASIC DOUBLET ANTENNA

The basic doublet is a probably the most useful simple multi-band antenna for amateur use. It is simple and yet effective, and requires no special earth or counterpoise arrangements. The only drawback is that the balanced feeder it uses cannot be routed trough a house, and like all tuned feeder antennas it requires the use of an ATU. Despite these minor disadvantages it has a tremendous amount to offer.

The arrangement for the antenna is shown in **Fig 4.3**. The antenna is essentially a balanced system and each half of the top plus each wire in the feed line must be equal in length. Referring to Fig 4.3, AB = CD and

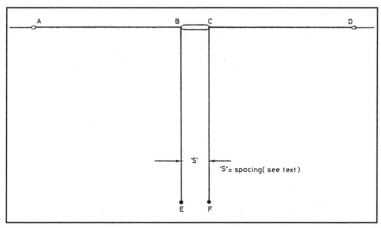

Fig 4.3 A basic doublet antenna, showing its inherent balance. The two legs of the top AB and CD are equal in length, as are the feeder wires BE and CF.

BE = CF. The antenna top is not cut to resonate at any particular frequency (unlike the half-wave dipole), and any length may be chosen to suit an individual location. When erecting an antenna of this nature there are no particular precautions to observe except that there are a number of feeder / top leg length combinations that should be avoided. These are summarised in **Table 4.1**.

A minimum top length of a quarter-wavelength (an eighth-wavelength for each leg) at the lowest contemplated operating frequency is suggested. Even when the total length of the top of the doublet antenna is a quarter-wavelength long, the antenna will still be an effective radiator. The section that is effectively the missing quarter-wavelength is taken up by the upper part of the feeder, so the antenna current in this section will cancel and not be radiated. This reduces the overall efficiency of the antenna but it will still tune up easily.

Where a total top length of 30.5m (100ft) is possible, a doublet antenna will work well on all the bands 3.5MHz to 28MHz and, if the feeders are strapped at their lower end and tuned against ground, it will also be effective on 1.8MHz. The radiation pattern in the horizontal plane will be similar to that of a half-wave dipole when it is used on 3.5MHz; as two half-waves in phase on 7MHz; as a 1.5-wavelength antenna on 14MHz with a six-lobed pattern of radiation; and progressively like a long wire on the higher-frequency bands with the lobes tending to align with the direction of the wire of the antenna.

Table 4.1 shows that when using doublet legs of 15.2m (50ft) together with 16.4m (54ft) of feeder there ought to be little difficulty with reactance on most amateur bands. There are of course many other combinations of top length and feeder length which can be chosen, either the feeder or the top being adjusted in length to suit individual locations.

TWO HALF-WAVES IN PHASE

If the top of a doublet is made from a pair of half-wavelength wires the antenna then becomes a simple collinear with some gain over a dipole. However, it should be remembered that gain in one direction will result in a lack of sensitivity in another. The radiation pattern will be similar to that of a dipole but it will more nearly resemble a narrowed figure 8, having a reduced radiation towards the ends of the wires. Its theoretical gain over a half-wave dipole is 1.9dB. To achieve a greater gain when

Band (MHz)	Lengths to be avoided (half the total top length plus feeder length)					
1.8 / 1.9	56.4m 185'	93.7m 307'	131m 430'			
3.6	29.26m 96'	48.8m 160'	68.3m 224'			
7	15m 49.5'	25.14m 82.5'	35.2m 115.5'	45.26m 148.5'		
10.1	10.5m 34.5'	17.52m 57.5'	24.53m 80.5'	31.54m 103.5'		
14.15	7.5m 24.75'	12.6m 41.25'	17.6m 57.75'	24.2m 79.25'	27.7m 90.75'	32.7m 107.25'
18.1	5.9m 19.5'	9.9m 32.5'	13.86m 45.5'	17.83m 58.5'	21.8m 71.5'	25.8m 84.5'
	29.7m 97.5'	33.7m 110.5'				
21.2	4.9m 16.25'	8.2m 27'	11.6m 38'	14.9m 48.75'	18.1m 59.5'	21.5m 70.5'
	24.7m 81'	28.0m 92'	31.4m 103'	34.8m 114'		
24.94	4.3m 14'	7.1m 23.25'	10m 32.75'	12.8m 42'	15.6m 51.25'	18.5m 60.75'
	21.3m 70'	24.1m 79.25'	27.1m 88.75'	29.9m 98'		
29	3.7m 12'	6.1m 20'	8.5m 28'	11m 36'	13.4m 44'	15.8m 52'
	18.3m 60'	20.7m 68'	23.2m 76'	25.6m 84'	28m 92'	30.5m 100'

Table 4.1 Lengths to avoid when designing multi band doublets with tuned feeders.

using two half-waves in phase, the spacing between the adjacent ends of the two half-wavelength wires must be about 0.45-wavelength. This spacing is easy to arrange when using separately fed, individual half-wave dipoles in phase, and then the gain over a single dipole becomes 3.3dB. To do this involves a pair of feed lines equal in length and a considerable space (at least 30m (100ft) on 14MHz). Fortunately there is a very effective and simpler substitute which has almost the same antenna gain; this antenna is known as the extended double Zepp.

THE EXTENDED DOUBLE ZEPP

By the simple expedient of lengthening both the doublet elements of an antenna consisting of two half-waves in phase, the effective spacing between the inner ends of the half-wave sections becomes greater. In this way, with an antenna top made from two 0.64-wavelengths, the effective spacing between the two half-waves becomes 0.28-wavelength. Dimensions for four amateur bands are given in **Table 4.2**.

Frequency (MHz)	0.5 wave	0.14 wave	Leg length (A+B)
7	20.34m	5.63m	26m
	66' 9"	18' 6"	85' 32"
14.2	9.98m	2.74m	12.64m
	32' 8"	9'	41' 8"
21.2	6.7m	1.82m	8.53m
	22'	6'	28'
28.5	5m	1.37m	6.4m
	16' 5"	4' 6"	21'

Table 4.2. Dimensions of the extended double Zepp.

This spacing gives a gain of about 3dB over a single half-wave dipole antenna. A gain of 3dB is equivalent to a doubling of the transmitted power and it is a very worthwhile feature of this antenna. **Fig 4.4** shows the extended double Zepp arrangement, and it will be noticed that the antenna currents in the added sections B and C, although in phase with each other, are opposed to the currents in the two longer half-wave sections of the top.

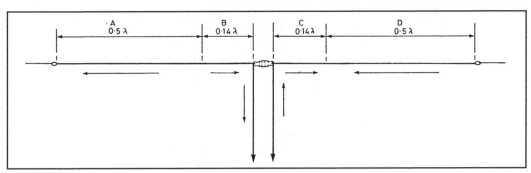

Fig 4.4 The design criteria for extended double Zepp antennas.

The power radiated by the centre sections contributes towards four weak lobes, each of which lies approximately 35° from the line of the wire top (see **Fig 4.5**).

An added bonus to be gained with this type of antenna is that it will also radiate well on other bands, but not of course as a two-element collinear. The 14MHz version will have a total top length of about 25.4m (83ft) and will behave as a long dipole on 7MHz. Even on 3.5 MHz, where each leg is about 8m (25ft) short of a quarter-wavelength, the antenna will still radiate effectively.

REFLECTORS FOR THE EXTENDED DOUBLE ZEPP

If a pair of parasitic wire reflector elements is located behind the half-wave sections of the extended double Zepp antenna, the radiation will then be mostly in one direction and the antenna gain will increase by almost another 3dB. This will give a total theoretical gain over a half-wave dipole of about 6dB (four times effective power). Such an arrangement requires two extra antenna supports and takes up more space but it would be a very useful antenna for consistent and regular DX working towards a particular country or station.

The spacing between the collinear elements and the reflectors should be about 0.15-wavelength, which is 3m (9ft 9in) on 14MHz, 2m (6ft 6in) on 21MHz, or 1.5m (4ft 10in) on 28MHz. The reflectors must be 10.7m (35ft 2in), 7.2m (23ft 6in) and 5.3m (17ft 6in) long respectively for the three wavebands. A nylon or similar cord running behind the centre 0.28-wavelength section of the double Zepp can be used to join and hold up the reflectors at their inner ends.

FOUR COLLINEAR ELEMENTS

The antenna illustrated in **Fig 4.6** is a particularly useful one for an operator who needs a bidirectional beam (fixed) which has a gain of about 4.3dB over a dipole. It is designed for the 28MHz band and its total length under 21m (70ft) is not excessive for many garden plots. It only has to be 6m (20ft) from the ground to perform well on its design frequency but naturally it benefits from being installed at a greater height because

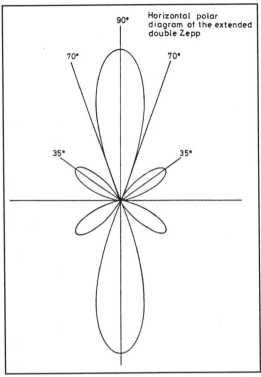

Fig 4.5 Horizontal polar diagram of the extended double Zepp.

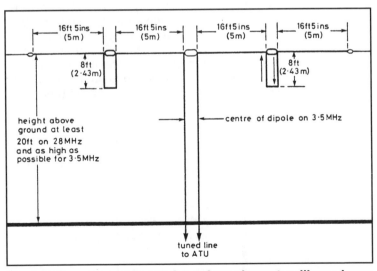

Fig 4.6 The measurements for a four-element collinear beam antenna designed for the 28MHz band which will also be a useful high-angle radiator on 3.5MHz.

of the reduced screening effects of buildings and trees etc. The use of two quarter-wave stubs adds to the total wire length and this makes each leg about 15.2m (50ft) long. On 3.5MHz the antenna is a short dipole, with its maximum current at the dipole centre some 5m (16ft) down the feed line. Being a low dipole on this band, it is only really useful as a high-angle radiator for semi-local contacts.

When used on its design frequency the currents in the half-wave elements are kept in phase by using quarter-wave shorted stubs. These are each 2.43m (8ft) long and their length was calculated bearing in mind the velocity factor of the wire pairs which make up each stub. If 300Ω ribbon is used for the stubs, another velocity factor of either 0.82 for the older flat ribbon or 0.87 for the slotted Bofa variety must be kept in mind. In the latter case the stubs must each be 2.13m (7ft) long.

Despite the fact that the RF current in the stubs cancel and do not give rise to any radiation, movement in the breeze will naturally cause the stubs to move and this can alter the load conditions. To prevent undue movement, it is recommended that small weights made from pebbles should be taped at the bottom of each stub. For very windy locations a small cord can be taken from each stub and anchored to a suitable point.

THE G5RV ANTENNA

Louis Varney, G5RV, originally designed his famous G5RV antenna in 1946, and later published some updates in the July 1984 edition of *Radio Communication*. During its life it has been one of the standard multi-band antennas with countless versions made either by individuals or commercially manufactured. The basic antenna can be seen in **Fig 4.7**, and from this it can be seen that it consists of a top radiating section of two 15.6m (51ft) legs. A section of open wire feeder 10.36m (34ft) long is then used to provide a match to either 75Ω coaxial or twin lead feeder. An ATU may also be substituted at the bottom of the open wire feeder to give a good match to coaxial feeder at this point as the match provided at the bottom of the open wire feeder is not always optimum. Even if an ATU is not used at this point, one should be used close to the transmitter to enable it to see a good match at all times.

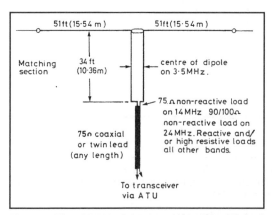

Fig 4.7 The G5RV antenna, showing critical dimensions and other details.

The antenna is able to be used on all the HF bands, performing in a number of different modes. On 1.8MHz the two feeder wires at the transmitter end are connected together or the inner and outer of the coaxial cable joined and the top plus 'feeder' used as a Marconi antenna with a series-tuned coupling circuit and a good earth connection.

On the 3.5MHz band, the electrical centre of the antenna commences about 5m (15ft) down the open line (in other words, the middle 10m (30ft) of the dipole is folded up). The antenna functions as two half-waves in phase on 7MHz with a portion 'folded' at the centre. On these bands the termination is highly reactive and the ATU must of course be able to take care of this if the antenna is to load satisfactorily and radiate effectively.

At 14MHz the antenna functions as a three half-wavelength antenna. Since the impedance at the centre is about 100Ω, a satisfactory match to the 75Ω feeder is obtained via the 10.36m (34ft) of half-wave stub. By making the height a half-wave or a full-wave above ground at 14MHz and then raising and lowering the antenna slightly while observing the standing wave ratio on the 75Ω twin-lead or coaxial feeder by means of an SWR bridge, an excellent impedance match may be obtained on this band. If, however, low-angle radiation is required, height is all important and, as most cables will withstand an SWR of 2 or greater, any temptation to improve the SWR by lowering the antenna should be resisted.

On 21MHz, the antenna works as a slightly extended two-wavelength system or two full-waves in phase, and is capable of very good results, especially if open-wire feeders are used to reduce loss. On 28MHz it consists of two three half-wavelength in-line antennas fed in phase. Here again, results are better with a tuned feeder to minimise losses, although satisfactory results have been claimed for the 10.36m (34ft) stub and 75Ω feeder.

When using tuned feeders, it is recommended that the feeder taps should be adjusted experimentally to obtain optimum loading on each band using separate plug-in or switched coils. Connection from the ATU to the transmitter should be made with 75Ω coaxial cable in which a harmonic suppression (low-pass) filter may be inserted.

With tuned feeders and use of lengths other than 32.1m (102ft) operation on the 10, 18 and 24MHz bands is possible, though some relatively high values of SWR can be expected. It should also be noted that the radiation pattern is of the general long-wire type and the position of lobes and nulls will vary with length and frequency.

Instead of simply bringing down a tuned line or ribbon feeder, G5RV arranged that there should be a 10.36m (34ft) matching section of open-wire feeder, which had connected to its lower end a length of either 75Ω impedance twin lead or 80Ω coaxial cable (see Fig 4.7). If 300Ω ribbon is used for the matching section, the old type must be cut to a length of 8.5m (28ft) and the slotted variety to a length of 9.3m (30ft 7in), which takes into account the different velocity factors of the two ribbons. Unfortunately the match to the coaxial or twin feeder at its junction with the lower end of the matching section is only good on 14MHz and 24MHz. If 50Ω coaxial is used the VSWR on these bands will rise to 1.8:1.

Louis Varney undertook many measurements on his antenna. Among these were details of the differing load presented to a 70Ω feeder at the point where the antenna joins the matching section:

    3.5MHz reactive load
    7MHz reactive load
    10MHz reactive load

14MHz resistive load, approx 90Ω
18MHz high-impedance load, slightly reactive
21MHz high-impedance load (resistive)
24MHz resistive load approx 90/100Ω
29MHz high-impedance load, slightly reactive.

In practical terms, if coaxial feeder is used, its weight will pull its centre down considerably, and it may be necessary to use a centre support and slope the antenna down on each side, to make an inverted-V. Doing this will alter the expected radiation patterns and it will also detune the antenna. ZS6BKW found that one effect of converting his antenna into an inverted-V was to change its resonant frequency. When being used on 14MHz, its frequency was lowered by 50kHz (which is a small change in frequency, only 0.3%) when the angle between the wires was decreased to 120°. This came down another 50kHz when the angle was sharpened to 85° although an angle as narrow as this is normally too acute for an inverted-V.

If a coaxial feeder is being used correctly as a 'flat' un-tuned line its characteristic impedance will be matched at each of its ends. If this is the case the coaxial cable may be safely buried along its run with no detriment to its operation. This can be useful when an antenna is located at a considerable distance from an operating position, but unfortunately the coaxial cable feed of a G5RV antenna must never be buried. The feeder is not correctly terminated and operates with standing waves along its length. It must thus be kept well away from metal and large objects.

The ZS6BKW computed design

ZS6BKW developed a computer program to determine the most advantageous length and impedance of the matching section and the top length of a G5RV-type antenna. The total top length of the antenna was reduced from 31.1m to 27.9m, and the matching section was increased from 10.37 multiplied by the velocity factor to 13.6 multiplied by the latter. This matching section must have a characteristic impedance of 400Ω which can be made up from a specially made length of open-wire line. A pair of 18SWG wires spaced 2.5cm (1in) apart will be suitable. This antenna gave the following SWR figures:

3.65MHz	11.8:1	poor
7MHz	1.8:1	good
10MHz	88:1	very poor
14MHz	1.3:1	good
18MHz	1.6:1	good
21.2MHz	67:1	very poor
24MHz	1.9:1	good
29MHz	1.8:1	good

The ZS6BKW antenna has reasonable SWR figures on five bands, which is an improvement on the original GSRV, but they are still not good enough to use the antenna without an ATU for correct matching.

MULTI-BAND DOUBLET FOR 10, 18 AND 24MHz
This antenna was deigned by Vince Lear, G3TKN, and first appeared in the June 1993 issue of *RadCom*. It outlines a design that is simple to erect, and can be ultimately fed with a coaxial feeder to facilitate easy installation by enabling the feeder to be routed as required rather than having to have a special lead in for twin feeder.

The multi-band doublet is shown in **Fig 4.8** covers the 10, 11 and 24MHz bands. It has a low impedance coaxial feed, and should require no ATU. In this respect it is particularly suitable for transceivers having solid state power amplifiers that normally require a well matched load if they are to deliver full power output.

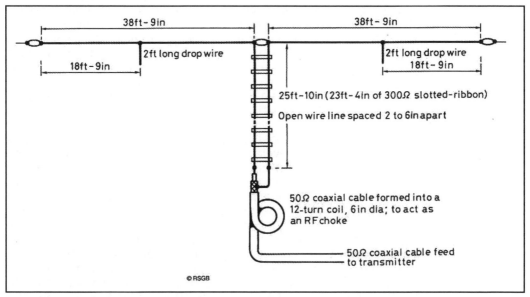

Fig 4.8 Diagram of the G3TKN multi-band doublet.

The antenna is simple to construct, lightweight, inexpensive, and requires little or no pruning. It should be of particular interest to those who already have a resonant antenna system for the other HF bands, and require just one antenna to cover all three so-called 'WARC bands'.

Theory of operation
If a point a quarter-wavelength or an odd number of quarter-wavelengths from the end of a wire is taken, it is found to have a maximum current, and this results in a low impedance. By checking some odd multiples of quarter-wavelengths for each of the WARC bands using the formula, L = 234 / f, where L = Length in feet of one quarter-wave and f = frequency in MHz, it can be seen that three quarter-wavelengths at 10.125MHz is 69ft 4in and five quarter-wavelengths at 18.1MHz is 64ft 7in and finally seven quarter wavelengths at 24.9MHz is 65ft 9in. These are all very close. In the multi-band doublet, the open wire line or 300Ω slotted ribbon stub operates with a standing wave on it in each case, and the total length of wire from one end of the antenna to the centre then down to

the base of the stub is such that a point of low impedance is achieved on each of the three bands. The antenna is optimised for an frequency of 18.1MHz, where the length from one end of the antenna to the centre then down to the base of the stub is five quarter-waves. On 10.1MHz it is a little short of three quarter-waves and on 24.9 MHz it is very close to seven quarter-waves.

To gain a better understanding of the antenna in terms of current distribution, radiation resistance, and radiation pattern, it is easier to analyse the operation of the aerial on each of the WARC bands.

10MHz operation

The current distribution on 10MHz is shown in **Fig 4.9**. From this we can see that each leg is 0.42-wavelength, and each half of the antenna carries in-phase currents, thus providing slight broadside gain. In other words it operates as two half waves in-phase, or a two-element collinear. The theoretical gain of two half-waves fed in-phase is 1.9dB. However, one could expect slightly less than this where the elements are slightly shorter, and hence where the current antinodes are closer together.

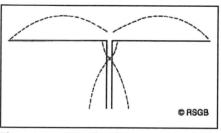

Fig 4.9 Current distribution on 10MHz.

Measurements with a well calibrated general coverage receiver and noise bridge placed at the bottom of an open wire (50mm / 2in spacing) stub indicated resonance around 9.9MHz, with the antenna at about 10m (30ft). A 300Ω slotted ribbon stub produced resonance at 9.7MHz. However, in both cases it was obvious by observation of the noise null that the antenna had a reasonably flat response between around 9.5 to 10.2MHz, and although at 10.1MHz the feed point could be expected to show slight inductive reactance (Ra+jX), no problems were encountered in practice. The antenna was fed with power from both a valve PA transmitter (Drake T4XC), and a TS-130S with solid state PA. The latter produced its normal power output without the need for any external ATU. SWR figures across the 10MHz band were around 1.1:1 measured at the transmitter end, and different lengths of coaxial feed line produced similar results indicating the line was operating in a flat condition.

The radiation pattern at 10MHz will be similar to a two element collinear array, maximum radiation being broadside to the wire, with a slightly narrower pattern than a dipole.

18MHz operation

On this band the antenna is three half-waves centre fed, and hence there is a low impedance point at the centre of the antenna. The stub, which is exactly half a wavelength at 18.1MHz, acts as a 1:1 impedance transformer, and simply transfers the low impedance seen at the centre of the antenna to the feed point at the base of the stub. It should be noted, however, that the impedance at the centre of multiple odd half-wavelength aerials increases slightly with the number of odd half-waves. In practice, no problems were encountered in this latter case, and SWR figures around

1.2:1 were obtained on the 18MHz band, with the TS-130S giving full output. The current distribution on 18MHz is shown in **Fig 4.10**.

The theoretical radiation pattern for a three half-wavelength antenna consists of four major lobes, each at 42° to the wire. The gain of each major lobe is in the region of 1dB compared with a dipole orientated to give maximum radiation in the direction of one of the main lobes.

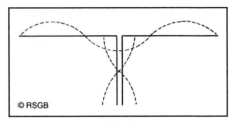

Fig 4.10 Current distribution at 18MHz.

24MHz operation

On 24 MHz, each leg of the antenna is approximately one wavelength, and the antenna functions as a two wavelength centre fed system. The current distribution is shown in **Fig 4.11**. However, when resonance was checked using the noise bridge, the antenna was found to resonate at 25.7MHz. This meant that the impedance at 24.9MHz would have a reactive component present, which would be capacitive, so that the impedance would be of the form (Ra-jX). The SWR

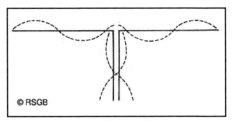

Fig 4.11 Current distribution at 24 MHz.

was in the region of 2:1, and while the T4XC transmitter with its valve PA would load into the antenna, problems were encountered with the TS-130S, which would not now deliver full output at 24.9MHz.

The antenna was lengthened slightly at the ends to bring its point of resonance nearer to 24.9MHz, but this produced an unacceptable match at 18MHz, and a very slight deterioration at 10MHz. It was therefore decided to attach short loading wires a half-wavelength (at 24.9MHz) from the ends of the antenna. This meant the loading wires were at points of high impedance at 24.9MHz, but points of lower impedance at 10 and 18MHz. As a result their effect was less on these latter two bands than it was on 24MHz operation.

In practice the resonant frequency was lowered from 25.7MHz to 25.2MHz using two 620mm (2ft) loading wires. Although there was a slight lowering of resonance on the 18MHz band, it did not cause any problems, and there was certainly no noticeable difference on 10MHz. The SWR obtained at 24.9MHz was 1.4:1, and the TS-130S was now delivering its full output.

The loading wires provide a means of pruning the antenna for the best compromise match on 18 and 24MHz, and depending on its height above ground, and general siting, it is probably worthwhile carrying out a little adjustment of these wires.

It is worth noting that when open wire line was used for the stub, the problem did not arise on 24MHz; the bandwidth appearing greater on each band. Therefore it is only worth fitting the loading wires if matching difficulties are encountered on the 24MHz band.

The radiation pattern at 24MHz will produce multiple lobes, tending towards the plane of the wire, but with slight gain in each of the major lobes.

RF choke balun

Two simple RF choke type baluns were tried, and both worked well. The first type was made by simply coiling up the coaxial feeder to make a 12-turn coil, 150mm) (6in) diameter at the point of connection to the base of the stub. The second type was one described by G2HCG in the May 1990 issue of *RadCom*. It is reproduced in **Fig 4.12**. It was found possible to just squeeze on 10 turns of UR43, wound as shown in the diagram. If UR43 50Ω cable is used throughout, no breaks in the cable are necessary until it joins onto the stub. However, UR67 heavy duty cable was used to keep losses to a minimum at 24MHz, and connection to the balun where UHF series connectors were used was very well weather-proofed.

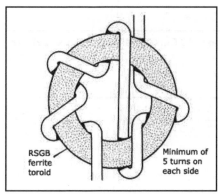

RSGB ferrite toroid

Minimum of 5 turns on each side

Fig 4.12 RF choke balun.

The simple choke balun is probably to be preferred for this antenna, as some slight reactance is present at 10 and 24MHz. Many of the commercial baluns are trifilar wound on a ferrite core, and while they work in a satisfactory manner into a resistive matched load, internal losses can increase if they are used where the load becomes reactive. However, a commercial W2AU type balun was tried both with the open wire line and 300Ω slotted ribbon stubs, with no noticeable drop in performance.

Construction

If the stub section is made from open wire line, this can use 16 - 18SWG wire, spaced anywhere from 50 to 150mm (2 to 6in). Spreaders may be easily made from sections of plastic curtain rail, or small diameter PVC piping. If plastic curtain rail is to be used for the spreaders, it is essential to make sure it is of all plastic construction and it has no metal strengthening rod running through the middle. Constructional details for the open wire line are shown in **Fig 4.13**.

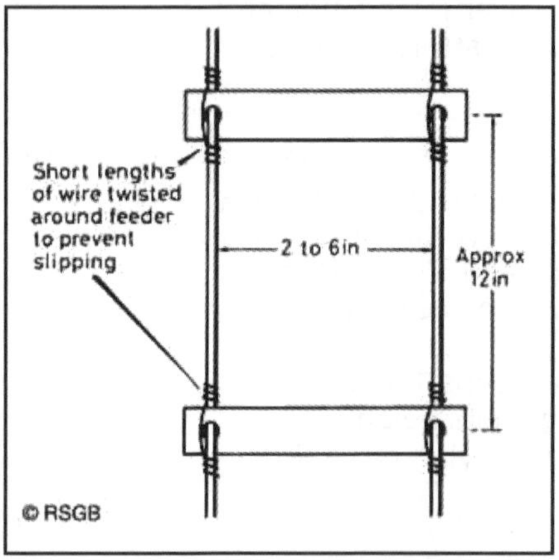

Short lengths of wire twisted around feeder to prevent slipping

2 to 6in

Approx 12in

© RSGB

Fig 4.13 Detail of open wire construction.

Slotted 300Ω ribbon feeder (type GMP6) offers another alternative for the stub, and is less obtrusive than open wire line. The solid dielectric 300Ω ribbon is not to be recommended as it absorbs moisture and this changes its characteristics and loss very considerably.

The 300Ω slotted ribbon was connected to the centre of the antenna using a short length of polypropylene cord, threaded through one of the slots in the feeder, to take the weight of the cable. This relieved mechanical strain at the soldered joints. A dipole T-piece was used to connect the ribbon to the coaxial cable via the RF choke balun. Again a small piece of cord was threaded through the slot in the ribbon to take the weight off the points of connection to the T-piece.

Operation on other bands

The doublet has also been used on all bands from 7 to 28MHz, by extending the stub into the shack and connecting to a balanced ATU. Although this takes away the principal advantage of the doublet using just one coaxial feed, it does offer the opportunity to extend its coverage. It should be remembered that when used in this way, the impedance offered to the ATU is dependent upon the length of open wire or slotted 300Ω ribbon feeder between the antenna and the ATU. An ATU with balanced antenna connections should be used.

On 7MHz the antenna is just short of a double extended Zepp. The double extended Zepp is basically two five-eighths wavelength sections fed in phase, and can offer 3dB gain over a dipole. Maximum radiation will be broadside to the plane of the antenna with a bi-directional lobe narrower than that expected from a dipole. On 21 and 28MHz the doublet offers multi-lobe radiation patterns in much the same way as it does at 24MHz.

F9GO MULTI-BAND DIPOLE

Although not strictly a tuned feeder antenna, as the matching is provided along the length of the feeder, this antenna probably fits best within this chapter as part of the feeder is tuned. The basic idea was originally devised by F9GO and appeared in *Radio-REF*.

The basic antenna (**Fig 4.14**) consists of a broadband dipole element about 8.3m (25ft) long. This is fed with 300Ω ribbon cable and has three compensating reactive networks along its length to ensure the correct match. The feeder beyond the reactive networks is non-resonant and can be extended to any required length. In the form described here the basic dipole can be used on the 7, 14, 21 and 28MHz bands.

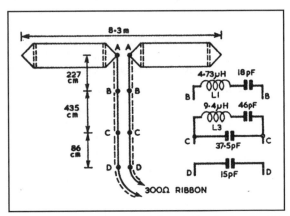

Fig 4.14 The F9GO multi-band dipole for 7, 14, 21, and 28 MHz with the associated reactive elements.

The broadband doublet on its own resonates at around 17MHz providing a capacitive load at frequencies below the resonant frequency, ie on the 7 and 14MHz bands. At frequencies above the natural resonant frequency of the doublet, it provides an inductive load. To overcome this, the networks shown in the diagram are added across the feeder at the points indicated.

The networks are easily constructed. L1 consists of 25 turns with a 15mm diameter, and 24mm long. L3 consists of 35.5 turns with a 15mm diameter and winding length of 28mm.

The networks are adjusted prior to fitting to give the correct reactance. The network B-B should be adjusted to give resonance with a dip meter at 17.2MHz when the terminals are shorted. The network C-C should resonate at 12MHz with the terminals open circuit and 7.8MHz with the terminals C-C shorted.

For adjustment of the feeder the antenna at A-A can be replaced by a 10Ω non inductive resistor in series with a 29pF capacitor for testing at 7.1MHz; a 51Ω resistor in series with 110pF for 14.2MHz; 150Ω resistor in series with a 1.8ìH inductor for 21.3MHz; and a 310Ω resistor in series with a 3.3ìH inductor for 28.4MHz.

It is suggested that the networks can be protected from the weather by using polythene bottles widely used for cleaning fluids. These can be cut to accommodate the networks and then rejoined to provide a weatherproof protection.

In use, the directivity appears to be less pronounced than that of a full length half-wave dipole on 7 or 14MHz and a little sharper on 21MHz, and rather like two half-waves in phase on 28MHz. The arrangement seems to offer a versatile multi-band antenna for restricted spaces and could also be used for portable operation.

G3LNP MULTI-BAND DIPOLE

Another interesting idea for a compact multi-band antenna was devices by Tony Preedy, G3LNP, and appeared in the March 1989 issue of *RadCom*. The antenna is shown in **Fig 4.15**. Here the short radiator ensures that the horizontal radiation is concentrated to the broadside on all frequencies from 7MHz to 30MHz. The entire radiating section is used on each band, and above the natural resonant frequency of 10.5MHz the antenna has some gain over a half-wave dipole.

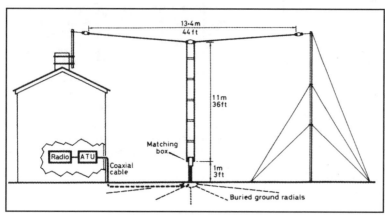

Figure 4.15 The G3LNP multi-band antenna.

Design details
The height of the radiator satisfies several criteria for optimum performance: 12m - 0.3-wavelength - is as high as one should erect a horizontal antenna for use on 7MHz and still expect full performance on short range contacts via near vertical incidence ionospheric reflection. Despite this, the antenna has been able to provide effective long haul communications. On 14MHz, the height is 0.6-wavelength and here the radiation maximum occurs at an elevation angle of approximately 25° and is best for intermediate distance propagation.

Comparisons on the air show that this antenna performs equally as well as a half-wave dipole at the same height and orientation on 7MHz. This is not unexpected, because with appropriate conductor diameter, there is nowhere for the input power to be lost except in the 600Ω feeder; and it, being of open construction, has negligible attenuation despite having a VSWR of almost 20.

The chosen height, in conjunction with the length of the dipole, also makes 3.7MHz operation feasible when the feeder wires are strapped and the antenna becomes a T-loaded quarter-wave vertical radiator. Performance in this mode is very much dependent upon the effectiveness of the ground system situated beneath the antenna, against which it is driven. Just how this influences radiation efficiency can be seen from the set of measurements in **Table 4.3** which show how the mean 3.7MHz field strength changed as the earth system was progressively improved.

Earth System	Relative field
Two copper rods driven 1 metre deep	0dB
Above plus 4 buried radial wires 14 metres long	+2.5dB
Above plus 16 buried radials 14 metres long	+3dB

Table 4.3 Relative field strengths for the antenna with different earth systems.

The length of the horizontal dipole was chosen because it is the maximum which will still maintain all of the radiation broadside to the wire at the highest working frequency of 30MHz. At this frequency a gain of 2dB over a half wave dipole is achieved.

Multi-frequency matching

To visualise the principle of the matching system consider one half of the dipole to be an extension of the 600Ω feeder, and to start with a total electrical length of a half-wave at 7MHz. As **Fig 4.16** shows, the impedance seen at the end of the feeder will be a pure but very high resistance at this frequency. At the harmonically-related frequencies of 14, 21 and 28MHz this point will also be resistive but the value will be progressively lower with increasing frequency. The actual value of this resistance is a function of both radiation resistance and the impedance-transforming action of the feeder. Because radiation resistance increases with frequency it causes the transformed resistance at this point to fall with increasing frequency.

If at 7MHz the measuring point is moved towards the antenna a place will be found where the resistance has dropped to 200Ω but this will be

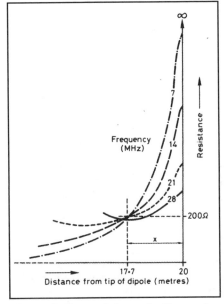

Fig 4.16 The resistance in the region of half a wavelength from the end of the dipole.

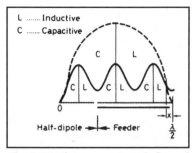

Fig 4.17 The current and sign of the reactance at fundamental and third harmonic showing that when X is less than four wavelengths the reactance is consistently inductive at the point where currents and hence resistances are equal.

accompanied by an inductive reactance of typically 800Ω. At harmonic frequencies the rate of change of resistance with electrical distance is progressively less, so that even though resistance was low at the half-wavelength point the value at the new measuring point still tends to look like 200Ω. A similar effect can be expected with the associated reactance, the magnitude of which roughly will be in inverse relationship to frequency and this is represented in **Fig 4.17**. A capacitor with a reactance of 800Ω will therefore cancel the feeder reactance at this point at 7MHz, and because the reactance of a capacitor is inversely proportional to frequency, it will nearly provide the correct reactance necessary for the harmonic frequencies.

Because the load is balanced, two capacitors are required - each of 400Ω reactance at 7MHz. When these are trimmed, they should provide simultaneously a perfect match at the 4:1 balun at, say, 7.1MHz, and an acceptably low VSWR on the harmonically-related bands. A simple pi-type ATU may be necessary at the transmitter end of the coaxial cable.

Practical points

Very high voltages are produced across the matching capacitors, particularly on 7MHz, so these need to be made from open sections of coaxial cable. Make them a little longer than necessary to provide a capacitance of 50pF. They can then be trimmed for minimum VSWR at a point in the middle of the 7MHz band. Resistors of 1MΩ are required to prevent the accumulation of static charges across the capacitors, as shown in **Fig 4.18**. Crocodile clips or U-links should be used to change between 3.7MHz and HF operation. The voltage here is almost certainly too high for switches or relays, unless specially high voltage types can be procured.

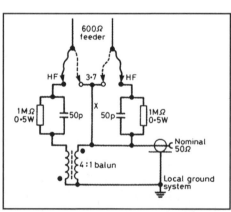

Fig 4.18 Matching box circuit showing the method of changing between 3.7MHz and the HF bands.

The capacitors are folded up and mounted in a weatherproof box, together with the balun.

The balun on the prototype consisted of five turns of twisted pair insulated wire on a large ferrite toroid obtained from a surplus supplier. Any proprietary type designed for the required frequency range and power would, of course, be suitable. The matching box should be fitted to a short wooden pole set into the ground, immediately below the centre of the dipole if possible.

Wire of 12 SWG, or equivalent size flexible wire is required for the dipole itself. In order to avoid using numerous spacers and excessive tension at the feeder the wire should be very flexible. The prototype used miniature coaxial cable 2.5mm in diameter and a spacing of 120mm. This has a plated steel inner conductor and will not stretch provided the inner and braid are joined at each end. Only two spacers were necessary.

Any length of low-impedance coaxial cable can be used to connect the transmitter or receiver to the antenna matching box.

Results
Actual impedances obtained vary between installations owing to proximity to buildings and ground conditions. As a guide of what can be expected **Table 4.4** gives some VSWR measurements taken on the 50Ω coaxial cable on the prototype installation.

The value of the capacitance at (a), where the 7MHz VSWR was sacrificed in order to improve the match at 28MHz, was 45pF. At (b) the capacitance was 50pF.

Frequency (MHz)	VSWR(a)	VSWR(b)
3.7	1.5	1.5
7.1	1.8	1.0
14.2	3.2	3.2
21.3	2.6	2.5
28.4	3.5	5.0

Table 4.4 VSWR measurements taken on the prototype antenna.

Making the capacitors
Cut the coaxial cable for the capacitors on the basis of 100pF / m for 50Ω solid-dielectric cable and seal the ends, after trimming, with self-amalgamating tape. The inner conductor should connect to the feeder and the braid to the balun, which is the low voltage side.

Using 75Ω cable
Some experiments were made to see what changes would be necessary to adapt the system for 75Ω cable. As might be expected from looking at Fig 4.16, a longer section of open-wire feeder is required and slightly less capacitance gave the best compromise VSWR over the bands. The feeder length is now 12m (39ft) and the capacitors were each 40pF. On the 80m band, resonance occurs at a lower frequency nearer the band centre. Results of VSWR measurement referred to 75Ω are shown in **Table 4.5**.

In each band it was possible to dispense with the ATU when using an old valve transceiver.

Frequency (MHz)	VSWR	Frequency (MHz)	VSWR
3.6	1.5	21.0	1.3
3.7	1.8	28.0	2.7
7.0	2.0	28.4	2.2
7.1	1.9	28.8	1.0
14.0	2.5	29.0	1.7
14.3	2.6		

Table 4.5 VSWR measurements for the antenna referred to 75Ω

Operation on other bands
The antenna will work on 10, 18 and 24MHz, but it does not then present a low VSWR. An ATU would be essential, and it would also be necessary to short-circuit the matching capacitors. Operation on 1.8MHz has not been attempted, but it should be possible, provided a suitable loading inductor is inserted at point X in Fig 4.18, and adjusted to bring the antenna to resonance in the band.

Chapter 5
Loops and Other Closed Circuit Antennas

Loops, or more correctly closed circuit antennas, are a popular form of antenna that can be used to good effect on the HF bands as well as other frequencies. These antennas fall into two basic categories, namely those that contain a total conductor length which is small when compared to a wavelength, and those which use a wavelength or more of conductor.

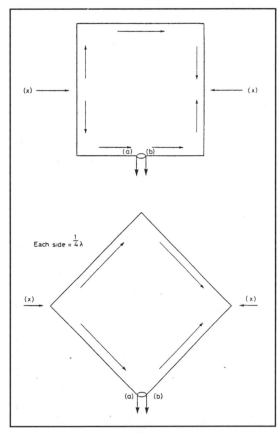

Fig 5.1 The instantaneous current distribution along the sides of a full-wave quad loop. When the loop is bottom-fed, as is shown in both these examples, its radiation will be horizontally polarised. The points x are at high impedance and voltage which means that the quad arranged as a diamond must have very good insulation at two of its corners 'x'.

TYPES OF LOOPS

Small loops can be likened to large coils, as they have a current distribution similar to that found in a coil: it is in the same phase and has the same amplitude in every part of the loop. To achieve this end, the total length of the conductor in such a loop must not exceed about 0.1-wavelength. Small loop antennas may be further categorised into single and multi-turn loops. One common example of the multi-turn loop is the ferrite rod antenna found in most medium-wave portable receivers.

The types that are used for transmitting generally fall into the single-turn loop category. These antennas have a number of disadvantages, but the idea of having a small yet effective antenna is very attractive to those who have very limited space for their antennas. These small loop antennas have a very low radiation resistance and a very high Q. This in turn implies a very narrow bandwidth.

To overcome the low radiation resistance very careful techniques are required to ensure that losses are minimised. It is also necessary to ensure that the antenna resonates on the right frequency. While it is theoretically possible to use an inductor, the resistance of the coil adds unacceptable levels of loss and therefore capacitors are always used instead. It is also necessary to ensure that the resistance of the loop itself is kept low. To achieve this, copper pipe is generally used as the basis for the antenna.

In view of their construction, small loops do not fall into the category of 'wire antennas' and therefore they are not covered here.

Antennas that are termed **large loops** are characterised by the fact that the current is not the same in all points around the loop. This gives rise to an entirely different set of properties and these can be exploited in a different way to those of small loops.

FULL-WAVE QUAD LOOPS

The full-wave quad (square) antenna has been a popular antenna for many years. The antenna can be considered to be derived from a 'pulled out' folded dipole. As such, it retains the RF current characteristics of such an antenna (see **Fig 5.1**) with in-phase currents along both its top and bottom sections. Each side of a quad is a quarter-wavelength long, and the antenna may be arranged either as a square or as a diamond. The two examples illustrated in Fig 5.1 are fed at their bases and they both show horizontal polarisation. When fed at a point half-way up either of their sides the polarisation will be vertical. The length of conductor used to achieve resonance in a quad is greater than just two half-wavelengths (285 / f (MHz) metres or 936 / f(MHz) feet), and instead the formula 306.3 / f (MHz) metres or 1005 / f (MHz) feet must be used when designing this type of antenna. Practical conductor lengths for quad antennas for use on the HF amateur bands are given in **Table 5.1**.

Quad characteristics

Unlike a folded dipole, the feed impedance of a quad is only about 100Ω. The antenna exhibits some slight gain over a half-wave dipole. The distance that the two current maxima are apart means that it acts like a pair of stacked dipoles. The direction of

Band(MHz)	Length of delta loop or quad	Length of each side Quad	Delta
3.6	85m 279' 1"	21.25m 69' 8"	28.33m 93'
7	43.76m 143' 6"	10.49m 35' 10"	14.58m 47' 10"
10.1	30.25m 99' 6"	7.58m 24' 10"	10.1m 33' 2"
14.15	21.64m 71'	5.41m 17' 9"	7.13m 23' 8"
18.1	16.92m 55' 6"	4.23m 13' 10"	5.64m 18' 6"
21.2	14.44m 47' 5"	3.61m 11' 10"	4.81m 15' 10"
24.94	12.55m 41' 2"	3.13m 10' 3"	4.18m 13' 9"
29	10.56m 34' 9"	2.64m 8' 8"	3.52m 11' 6"

Table 5.1. Practical conductor lengths for quad and delta antennas.

maximum radiation is at right angles to the plane of the quad loop (ie looking through the loop shows the directions of greatest radiation). The gain should be about 1dBd, which represents a power gain in two directions of 1.26 times, a useful feature of the single-loop quad antenna. There are quite deep nulls in the plane of the loop, which are more pronounced than the nulls off the ends of a dipole.

A further advantage of the quad is that being a closed loop it is less susceptible to the effects of the ground than a half-wave dipole. At a height above the ground of a half-wavelength (1/2-wavelength), the main radiation lobes of a quad antenna are about 4° lower than those of a half-wave dipole at the same height. At 3/8-wavelength the radiation angle is almost 10° lower. At a quarter-wavelength above ground most of a dipoles radiation will be upwards, but a full-wave quad has its main radiation lobes 40° above the horizon. This represents a 'first skip' distance of about 400 miles.

The influence of near objects such as trees or buildings on the characteristics of quad antennas is small. This means that such antennas

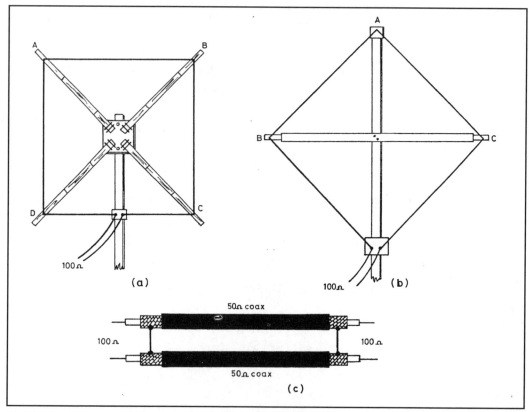

Fig 5.2 (a) A square quad arrangement using bamboo spreaders. The RF voltages will not be high at the points where the wires are fixed to the bamboos, so no special insulating arrangements are needed. (b) With this arrangement point A is at low impedance but points B and C will require good insulation. (c) Two equal lengths of 50Ω impedance coaxial cable can be connected in this way to provide a balanced 100Ω feeder for a quad antenna.

can often be used to good effect even when located in house roof spaces etc.

Practical quad loops

The two basic configurations for quad antennas are given in **Fig 5.2**. When arranged as a square, as in Fig 5.2(a), bamboo or glass-fibre spreaders (or 'spiders') are needed. The high-voltage points along the antenna are at the centre points of the vertical wire sections, and therefore well away from the ends of the spreaders at A, B, C and D. The impedance at these corner points is not high and therefore little in the way of insulation is needed where the wire is tied to the spreaders.

If bamboo is used, it should be waterproofed by the application of several coats of polyurethane varnish. Despite the shiny appearance of this wood, it will, if untreated, rapidly absorb moisture and will rot. The ends of any piece of bamboo will also need special weatherproofing treatment. The centre block shown in Fig 5.2(a) can be made from thick Perspex or 12mm (0.5in) marine plywood. If wood is used it *must* be varnished. A pair of 'U' bolts can be used to hold each spreader in position, and a small rectangle of almost any kind of insulating material (so long as it is weatherproof) will suffice at the feed point.

The arrangement in Fig 5.2(b) will need more space, for its height and width are the diagonals of a square. Furthermore, the RF voltages and impedances will be high at points Band C. This means that there must be good insulation at these positions. Small ceramic 'stand-off' insulators or similar can be used at A and at the ends of the wooden cross bar. The feed point insulation is not critical, as it is at a relatively low impedance, and here even a well-varnished block of hardwood should serve.

A dip oscillator can be used to check a quad for resonance. A single-turn coil across the feed point (feeder removed) can be coupled to this piece of test equipment to determine quad tuning.

The quad feed impedance of 100Ω is awkward to match with commonly available feeder. In order to avoid the use of tuned stubs or matching transformers, one simple way to feed such an antenna is by employing two equal lengths of 50Ω coaxial cable (see Fig 5.2(c). This arrangement will provide a 100Ω balanced feed line which can easily be matched to the equipment via an ATU. This type of line, as it is made up from coaxial cable, can be safely buried. Of course, open-wire tuned feeder (or 300Ω ribbon used as tuned line) may be used but only with an ATU.

The 1dB gain of a single-element quad loop makes it a useful and simple bi-directional antenna, and it only need be turned through 90° to realise all-world coverage. Its deep nulls are also useful and can be utilised to reduce the strength of unwanted signals.

FULL-WAVE DELTA LOOPS

A delta loop is also a closed-loop antenna and it contains a wavelength of conductor wire. It has several features which are common to the quad antenna. A delta loop is normally arranged in the form of an equilateral triangle, having either one side at the top or at the base. Delta loops are popular for use on the low bands (1.8, 3.5 and 7MHz) because they are much easier to set up mechanically than a quad antenna and this is particularly important at these frequencies in view of their size. However, they have a smaller internal area than a quad which reduces slightly their comparative gain.

An equal-sided delta-loop antenna will show a gain of about 0.5dB less than a quad (ie 0.5dB over a dipole) and the two sloping sides of the delta will only contribute a third of the radiated power. The remaining two-thirds come from the horizontal side.

There are five basic arrangements for the orientation and feeding of delta loops. These are shown in **Fig 5.3**. Types (a), (c) and (d) will give horizontal

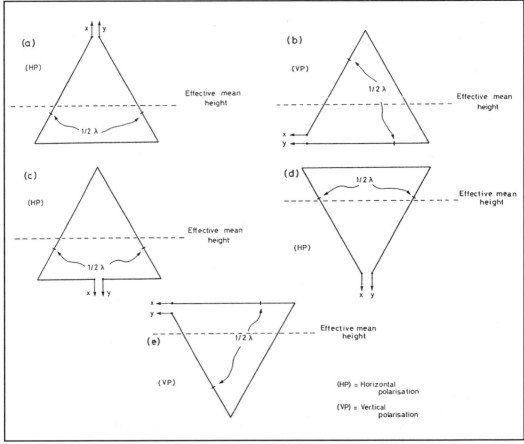

Fig 5.3   **Five different delta loop configurations. The arrows indicate the high-voltage points at the ends of each half-wave. Versions (d) and (e) provide the best effective height above ground for a given mast height. The two vertically polarised versions shown in (b) and (e) are the best for long-distance work, for they both have their maximum radiation at low angles to the horizon. Types (a) and (c) have high-angle radiation (80°) and would be more suitable for short-distance communications. The delta loop at (d) has a radiation angle of about 47° and will normally have a first-skip range of 400 miles.**

polarisation and (b) and (e) will have vertical polarisation. The geometry of a delta loop, which may be used with either a horizontal side at its top or its base, determines the effective mean height of the antenna. This effective height is greatest when one of the delta sides is positioned at the top.

The half-wave ends (ie the points of high voltage and impedance) are indicated in each of the five arrangements shown in Fig 5.3. The true effective mean height may be calculated as follows:

When one side is at the top, the effective height is the height from ground to the highest point of the antenna minus a 12th of a wavelength. When one side is at the base, the effective height is the height from ground to the highest point minus a quarter-wavelength.

The total conductor length in a delta loop is the same as an equivalent quad at the same frequency, ie 306.3 / f (MHz) metres or 1005 / f (MHz) feet . Like a quad, the maximum radiation from a delta loop is at right angles on both sides of the plane of the loop. Its feed impedance will range from about 70Ω in the case of an equilateral delta to more than 100Ω when the antenna is flattened somewhat. Another similarity to a quad is the delta's pair of radiation nulls in the plane of the antenna.

Performance

The performance of quad and delta-loop antennas is largely determined by their height above ground. Each of these antennas has an 'effective mean height', and this equates with the height of a half-wave dipole above ground when it is cut for the same band. In the case of a quad antenna the effective mean height will be at a point half way up its vertical wires. For long-distance communications a half-wave dipole should ideally be at least a half wavelength above ground and this distance will still apply when considering the effective mean heights of loops.

The radiation angles of delta loops are also greatly influenced by their physical arrangement and the positions of their feed points. Only two of the five delta loops illustrated in Fig 5.3 are really useful for DX working. Type (b) has its maximum radiation at 27° and type (e) has an angle of only 20°. Both of these loop types are vertically polarised.

The horizontally polarised versions (a), (c) and (d), however, have radiation angles to the horizon of 80° and 47° respectively. This means that types (a) and (c) are useful for short range communication. Type (d) will have a 'first-skip' range of about 400 miles, whereas the two vertically-polarised deltas (b) and (e) will have first skip ranges of 600 miles and almost 1000 miles.

Unfortunately type (e), which is the best for DX work, needs two supports and it also has an inconveniently positioned feed point. Type (b), which only requires a single support and has its feed at one lower corner, is the best configuration for ease of construction when a large delta loop is contemplated for use on one of the low bands.

Practical delta loops

Two of the several ways to set up a delta-loop antenna are given in **Fig 5.4**, with both of these being 14MHz designs. The example shown in (a) has a mean effective height of almost a half-wavelength, and is arranged to provide low-angle radiation. The rather awkward position of the feed point is overcome when it is placed not too distant from the house. The feeder should not drop down vertically when using this arrangement or it will unbalance the system and detune the antenna.

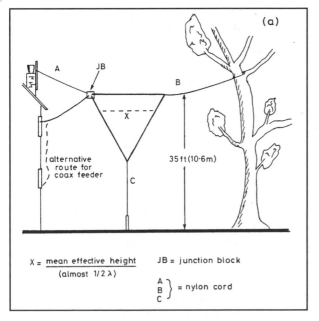

In Fig 5.4(b) a single 10m (33ft) support pole is all that is needed. The lower ends of the delta are held in position by nylon cords. In this antenna arrangement the feeder can safely drop down and run along at ground level or be buried. Conventional insulators are not required as the voltages at the corner angles of delta-loop antennas are not high. Nylon or Terylene cords are fine as both insulators and supports. The junction blocks are also located at points of low RF potential and as a result they can be made from almost any insulating material that will shed moisture.

A variation of the antenna shown in (b), which can be used when the physical size of the loop and its support are very large at the lower frequencies (7 or 3.5MHz), is one where the two upper sides of the loop come down from the centre support at an angle of about 45°. This will allow the use of a shorter support mast and on 7MHz a mast height of about 15m (50ft) will suffice.

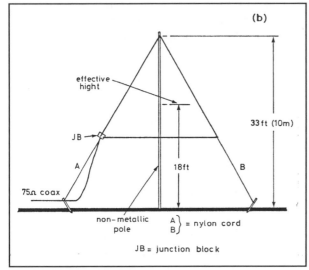

Fig 5.4 (a) A practical delta-loop antenna for 14MHz based upon the type shown in Fig 5.3(e). It is suspended from two supports. Its radiation angle is only 20°. (b) This version uses a single support mast and is the arrangement shown in Fig 5.9(b). Its effective height is, however, only 18ft (5.5m) whereas the antenna shown in (a) has an effective height of almost a half-wavelength.

Trees can also be employed as delta-loop supports, and some amateurs have had fine operating results when the complete loop was positioned actually inside the branch system of large trees. Such antennas virtually disappear through the summer months and fortunately the leaf growth does not seem to affect their performance to any great degree.

Fig 5.5 illustrates a suitable connection block for delta loop antennas. Almost any insulating material which is weatherproofed will do for this - the actual end of the coaxial feeder cable and the soldered connections must also be thoroughly weatherproofed. The use of 75Ω coaxial feeder (which must be taken to an ATU when 50Ω input / output equipment is used) is not essential, and, like many other antennas so far described, a tuned feed line can be employed.

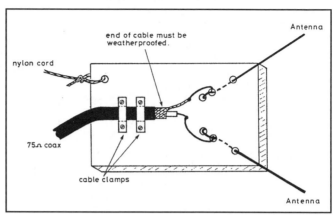

Fig 5.5 A suggested connection block for delta-loop antennas.

GM3AXX COMPACT MULTI-BAND DELTA LOOP

A very interesting and useful delta loop antenna appeared in the January 1987 'Technical Topics' with an idea from Alasdair Fraser, GM3AXX. The idea is for a compact four-band delta loop antenna that can be fed directly from coaxial cable without an ATU yet which fits into a small garden. Since inductive loading is required only on 10MHz the efficiency is reasonably good and the only problem appears to be the need to go outside to the switch box when changing bands. However, even this minor problem could be overcome with the aid of a high-voltage remote controlled three-position switch or two DPST relays.

The theory is extremely simple: a full-wave on 14MHz is approximately the same physical length as a half-wave on 7MHz or 1.5-wavelengths on 21MHz. Originally, when 10MHz was released, GM3AXX fitted a small loading coil to his 14MHz delta loop antenna and found this to work remarkably well. Since then he has modified the loop as shown in **Fig 5.6** to include 7 and 21MHz operation. If the 10MHz facility is not required it would be possible to use a larger loading coil for 3.5MHz operation, although inevitably this would have the effect of lowering the radiation resistance, increasing the Q (thus narrowing the bandwidth) and significantly lowering the efficiency on that band. For this reason, 1.8MHz loading is not recommended, although it would certainly enable operation on that band.

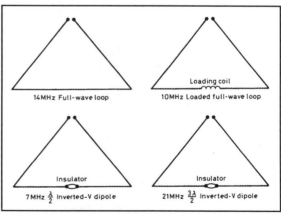

Fig 5.6 The concept of configuring a 20.13m (66ft) delta loop for use on 7, 10, 14, and 21MHz.

Construction and adjustment

The construction and adjustment of the antenna can be undertaken in a number of easy stages.

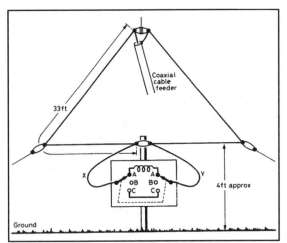

Fig 5.7 Practical construction of the GM3AXX's four-band antenna. However, note that having the base wire only 1.22m (4ft) above ground would breach safety recommendations except when used for very low-power transmissions.

(1) Make a 14MHz delta loop using two 10.07m (33ft) lengths of wire. Suspend the loop at its apex about 6 to 7.5m (20 to 25ft) above ground. Connect coaxial cable to apex (with or without balun) and run the cable (any length) to an SWR bridge / transceiver. The base corners are connected via insulators to a convenient garden fence or similar, so that the base section is about 1.2m (4ft) above ground (it needs to be higher if there is any risk of people touching these wires, as they carry a high RF potential).

(2) Make up a ground post with insulator at the top and the switch box near the top. The insulator separates the two sections of the loop.

(3) With switch in position 'C' adjust lengths of stubs X, Y until loop resonates (ie shows low SWR) at 14050kHz (for CW operation), 14250kHz (for SSB operation), or 14200kHz(for both).

The switch box should be waterproof. It contains the two-pole, three-way switch (which needs to withstand high RF voltages except for really low-power operation). Switch positions are: A for 10MHz, B for 7 and 21MHz and C for 14MHz.

It should be stressed that, except on very low power, the wires X and Y connected to the switch will be at high RF voltage, particularly on 7 and 21MHz, and that this needs to be taken fully into account where there is any possibility of anyone else, especially young children, having access to these wires.

THE 'LAZY QUAD'

Although it is superficially similar to a quad antenna in that it is a full-wave loop, the 'Lazy Quad' is in fact a close relative of the Kraus, W8JK, beam. Unlike a quad it is held in a horizontal plane and **Fig 5.8** shows a plan view of the antenna. The centre of the loop is broken by an insulator so it therefore becomes two half-waves, each of which is end-fed. The feed impedance is very high and typically about 9000Ω and as a result a low-impedance feeder cannot connect directly to it. The antenna has its maximum radiation in two directions and it is horizontally polarised. The gain over a half-wave dipole at the same height is 4dB.

Feed arrangements

The ideal arrangement uses a quarter-wavelength long matching transformer made with 675Ω impedance open-wire line which will provide a 50Ω balanced output impedance. At this 50Ω point a 1 : 1 balun must be used to allow the connection of any length of a standard 50Ω coaxial cable. However, it is still wise to use an ATU in the line to ensure that a suitable match is seen by the transmitter output devices.

The quarter-wave transformer is a relatively easy way to provide impedance step-down or step-up ratios, and its own impedance can be calculated from the formula:

Quarter-wave transformer impedance = √(Antenna impedance x Feeder impedance)

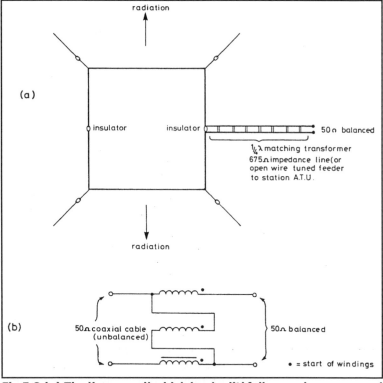

Fig 5.8 (a) The 'lazy quad' which is a 'split' full-wave loop arranged to lie horizontally. Its very high feed impedance makes matching to a 50Ω feeder difficult. An open-wire tuned feeder can be used instead of the quarter-wave matching transformer shown. (b) The circuit of a trifilar-wound, 1:1 ratio, unbalanced-to-balanced (or vice-versa) balun. A ferrite rod core is suitable for this balun if moderate power levels are used.

As this antenna has a feed impedance of about 9000Ω, the impedance of a suitable matching quarter-wave transformer is the square root of 9000 x 50Ω which is approximately 675Ω. The length of the quarter-wave section is calculated from the free-space length of an electrical quarter-wave at the operating frequency, which is then multiplied by the velocity factor of the line to be used. A well-constructed open-wire line will have a velocity factor of about 0.97, so the length of a suitable matching transformer can be found from:

$$\frac{246 \times 0.97}{f\ (MHz)}\ (feet)$$

For operation on 21.1MHz the length of such a quarter-wave matching transformer will be 3.42m (11ft 3in), and on 29MHz it is 2.51m (8ft 3in). A 675Ω impedance line is easily made using 18 SWG wire with a spacing of 180mm (7in).

Construction and setting up
The length of each half-wave element in this antenna (ie half the length of the perimeter) is 7.03m (23ft 8in) when cut for operation on 21.2MHz

and on 29MHz they are each 5.19m (17ft 4in). The insulation at the four comers is not very important, for these are not high voltage points. The insulation at the feed point and also at the other ends of the half-waves must be good and the use of glass insulators is suggested.

A 'lazy quad' for use on 29MHz only has sides that are only 2.64m (8ft 8in) long, and a rotatable version using bamboo spreaders would be sufficiently compact for many locations. Even on 21MHz the diagonal spreaders could be made with four 2.6m (8ft 6in) lengths of bamboo or glass fibre rod or tube.

One easy way to tune the antenna is to use a dip meter. A shorting bar (which can be conveniently made from two crocodile clips) is connected across the end of the 675Ω matching section. When the dip meter is coupled to the shorting bar the resonant frequency of the antenna can be measured. By moving the shorting bar along the line, a point will be found which indicates resonance at the required frequency and then the unwanted wires can be cut and removed together with the temporary shorting bar. If open-wire or ribbon feeder is used as a tuned line to feed this antenna there is no need to tune the antenna to resonance; any discrepancy will be taken up within the feeder system.

A suitable 1:1 balanced-to-unbalanced, trifilar-wound balun can be made in a similar fashion to that shown in Fig 3.13 (Chapter 3). Three, instead of two, lengths of enamelled wire must be bound tightly together before winding them on to the ferrite-rod core. Fig 5.8(b) shows the connections to the balun windings; any length of 50Ω coaxial cable can be connected to the 'unbalanced' end of the balun. The SWR should be better than 1.5:1 over a bandwidth of 400kHz centred upon the design frequency of 21.2MHz. This bandwidth will be greater for antennas centred on 29MHz.

THE BI-SQUARE ANTENNA

The bi-square antenna is another loop antenna and from its appearance in **Fig 5.9** it can be seen that it is similar in appearance to the 'lazy quad'. However, the antenna is a broadside two-wavelength broken loop set up in the vertical plane. The bi-square antenna has gain in two directions at right angles to the plane of the loop of about 4dB over a half-wave dipole and it only needs a single support. This needs to be 11m (36ft) high for an antenna designed for 21MHz and only 8.6m (28ft) high for a 29MHz version. The total loop wire length is 2 x 960 / f (MHz) feet and the antenna is set up in the form of a diamond.

Each side of the bi-square has equal horizontal and vertical radiation components. The latter cancel and leave four horizontal sources which are in phase. This means that the antenna radiation is horizontally polarised at the design frequency but when it is used at half the design frequency there is end-fire directivity and vertical polarisation. At half-frequency the gain reduces to about 2dBd and the antenna will not have its normal 1000Ω feed impedance. To get the best results this antenna must be at least a metre (3ft) above ground and preferably from 3 to 3.5m (10 to 12ft) above electrical ground.

The bi-square is best fed with a tuned line, but for single band operation a quarter-wave matching transformer can be employed. A reasonable match to 75Ω will be achieved if a length of 300Ω ribbon feeder is used as the stub or matching section because the impedance will actually be in the region of 80 - 90Ω and this approach simplifies its preparation. When a 75Ω coaxial feeder is used a 1:1 balun should be connected between this and the quarter wave transformer.

A 21.2MHz bi-square has two sides of equal length, each one being 13.78m (45ft 3in) long, while on 29MHz they reduce to 10.1m (33ft 2in). If slotted 300Ω ribbon is used to make up the matching transformer, it will be either 3.04m (10ft) long for 21MHz or 2.14m (7ft 4in) for 29MHz. The older un-slotted and less satisfactory type of ribbon feeder has a different velocity factor of 0.8 and it will have to be cut to shorter lengths. As a final note it is necessary to remember that good insulation is needed at all the four corners of a bi-square because these points carry high voltages and represent a high impedance.

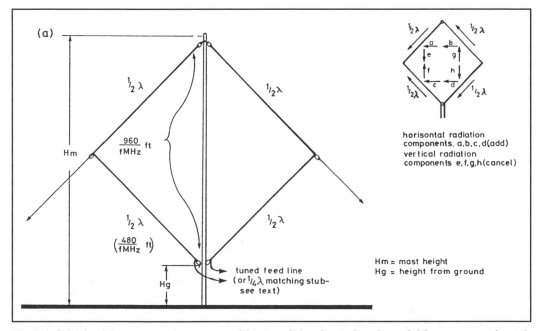

Fig 5.9 (a) The bi-square antenna provides useful gain. It is a broadside two-wavelength loop set up in the vertical plane. It can be used at half-frequency with reduced gain and it will then have a different radiation pattern. (b) The instantaneous current distribution along a bi-square antenna. The horizontal radiation components add and the vertical components cancel. Radiation is therefore horizontally polarised and is in two directions, ie looking through the loop.

Chapter 6
End Fed Wire Antennas

A single length of wire fed from one end is perhaps the simplest antenna type available to the radio amateur. In their simplest terms the longest piece of wire that can be strung up as high as possible usually produces some reasonable results. An ATU can then be used to ensure a good match to either the feeder or the transmitter or receiver that is to be used. However, like most things in this world, all is not quite so simple as it first seems, and this presents some interesting points and challenges to the would-be end fed wire user.

One of the major points when using an end fed wire is that the wire radiates as soon as it leaves the tuning unit. This means that high levels of RF may exist in the vicinity of the radio shack. This has disadvantages from two viewpoints. The first is that there is a growing awareness of the possible dangers of radio frequency radiation from a health standpoint. Secondly high levels of RF can give rise to feedback if the radiation can be picked up by power leads, microphone leads and the like.

As such it is best to adopt one of a number of strategies. It may be that the end fed wire is only needed for receiving, or for low power transmissions. Otherwise it may be possible to have a remote ATU which is fed from the shack by coax. In this way it is possible to remove the regions of the antenna carrying the high levels of RF away from inhabited areas, thereby avoiding health risks.

WIRE LENGTH AND IMPEDANCE

The impedance of the wire is of particular importance because ultimately a good match will need to be presented to the transmitting and receiving equipment. It is possible to look at what the impedance of a random length of wire might present at its feed point. All wires display a high impedance at their far ends at any frequency. This fact makes it a simple matter to work forwards along the wires in half-wavelengths or quarter-wavelengths to determine the approximate impedance at the feed points. A quarter-wavelength back from the remote open end will have a low impedance, and a half-wavelength back will have a high impedance.

Some impedances are difficult to match with an ATU, particularly those which are very high or low, so it is prudent to arrange that such conditions are not present at the ATU end of an end-fed wire. Lengths of wire which are close to odd multiples of a quarter-wavelength (or just less than this) are particularly bad, and the latter lengths will display a capacitive reactance which needs to be tuned out. When a long end-fed wire is used as a multi-band antenna it is almost impossible to determine a length which will avoid some reactance on one or more bands, but this reactance can be quite easily tuned out by using either an inductor (for capacitive reactances) or a capacitor (for inductive reactances) between the wire end and the ATU.

RADIATION PATTERNS

End fed wire antennas exhibit some interesting directional radiation patterns. A single-wire antenna which is two half-wavelengths or more long will have alternate half-wavelengths out of phase. When wires are very long in terms of wavelength, the half-wavelengths along their length will also have different amplitudes of current, these currents diminishing along the wire.

Long wires produce quite complex multi-lobe radiation patterns, unlike the simple radiation lobes produced by collinear antenna systems. The longer the wire is made in terms of wavelength the more the main lobes tend to align with the axis of the antenna. There are also an increasing number of minor lobes in other directions as the wire length becomes greater. In **Fig 6.1**, (a) shows the horizontal radiation pattern for a horizontal wire, two wavelengths long. The four main lobes are marked A, B, C and D, and their effective power is about 5dB greater than the radiation from the four minor lobes.

When the wire length is increased to five wavelengths (Figure 6.1 (b)) there are still four main lobes but these are aligned closer to the line of the antenna wire (each being 22° from this line). There are additionally 16 minor lobes, the weaker of which are almost 10dB down from the main lobes. In both these examples, and with all long-wire antennas, there are deep nulls at right angles to the wire.

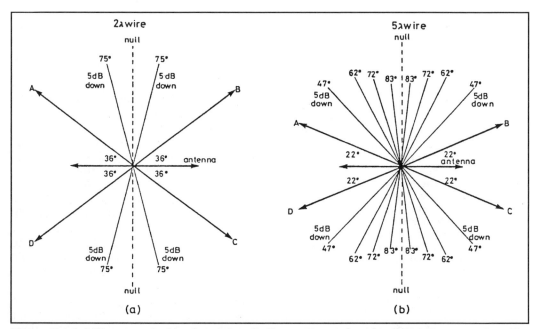

Figure 6.1 (a) The expected horizontal radiation pattern of a wire that is two wavelengths long. (b) A five-wavelength wire has its four main lobes closer to the line of the wire and has more minor radiation lobes.

If a long-wire antenna is at least half a wavelength above the ground at its lowest DX frequency, the angles of radiation in the vertical plane be low, and usually between 10 and 15° above the horizon. A single wire which is five wavelengths long will have power gain over a dipole (22° from the line of the long wire) of more than two times (4dB). This wire, when used on the 28MHz band, will become 10 wavelengths long will show a gain of 7.4dB. The maximum gain will then be in directions closer to the run of wire.

Wires which are 10 or more wavelengths long radiate mostly from their ends and they should therefore be aligned towards the preferred direction. In terms of gain for money spent, a long single wire antenna can have an advantage over a multi-element Yagi beam, but of course it cannot be rotated. To achieve world coverage, the long wire enthusiast will need several wires running in different directions to provide the right coverage. This may require a very large amount of ground. Obviously the gain is of no use if it is not aligned in the required direction.

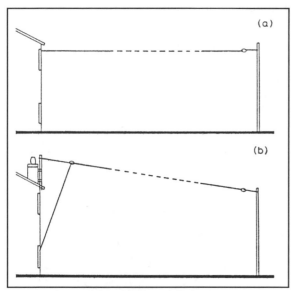

(a)

(b)

Fig 6.2 (a) A horizontal end-fed wire which will have little radiation in the vertical plane. On its harmonic frequencies there will be pronounced nulls at right angles to the wire. (b) A similar wire but the sloping section will allow some vertically polarised radiation and tend to spoil the expected radiation pattern of a long wire operating on its harmonic frequencies. The nulls at right angles to the wire will not be so pronounced.

PRACTICAL END-FED WIRES

Two physical arrangements for end-fed wire antennas are shown in **Fig 6.2**. The wire in Fig 6.2(a) is virtually horizontal along its length, and will show little if any radiation which is vertically polarised. Also being relatively high there will be challenges in ensuring a good earth arrangement, as discussed later.

In Fig 6.2(b) the wire slopes up from a downstairs window to a high point and then runs down at a small angle to the end support. If the near-vertical part of such an antenna is just a small proportion (say one-tenth) of the main top length it will have little effect upon performance, although there must be some radiation (vertically polarised) from the descending 'feed' wire. This vertically polarised section will fill in the nulls in the radiation pattern but additionally may induce some TVI or other EMC problems. The gradually sloping top will lower the angle of radiation towards the far end of the antenna and most of the radiation will also be in that direction.

End fed wires which are 9 to 12m (30 to 40ft) above ground will be very effective on 14MHz and the other bands higher than this frequency. Their DX performance on the higher bands will not, however, be matched on lower bands such as 7 and 3.5MHz. Here they will have much higher angles of radiation and will therefore be more suited for medium distance and short-haul communication.

END FED WIRE LENGTHS

The individual wavelengths away from the ends of a long wire do not join on to insulators, so their calculated lengths do not have to take into consideration the 'end effect'. They will therefore be closer to the theoretical free-space lengths. The lengths in feet and metres of wires up to 10 wavelengths long on the 14, 21 and 28MHz bands are given in **Table 6.1**. On other frequencies the lengths can be calculated by using the expression:

$$\text{Length (feet)} = \frac{984\,(N - 0.025)}{\text{Freq (MHz)}}$$

where N is the number of full wavelengths in the antenna. To calculate the lengths in metres use:

$$\text{Length (metres)} = \frac{300\,(N - 0.025)}{\text{Freq (MHz)}}$$

Number of wavelengths in the Antenna wire	14.15 MHz	21.2 MHz	28.5 MHz
1	20.66 m 67' 9"	13.79 m 45' 3"	10.25 m 33' 8"
2	41.86 m 137' 4"	27.9 m 91' 8"	20.78 m 68' 2"
3	63.0 m 206' 10"	42 m 138' 0"	31.3 m 102' 8"
4	84.25 m 276' 5"	56.2 m 184' 6"	41.83 m 137'3"
5	105.4 m 345' 11"	70.37 m 230' 11"	52.35 m 171' 9"
6	126.6 m 415' 6"	84.5 m 277' 4"	62.87 m 206' 4"
7	147.8 m 485' 0"	98.67 m 323' 9"	73.4 m 240' 9"
8	169 m 554' 7"	112.8 m 370' 2"	83.9 m 275' 4"

Table 6.1   Resonant lengths for end fed wires

A long wire must be at least two wavelengths long to show noticeable gain (about 1.3dB) over a half-wave dipole, and until it is four wavelengths long its gain remains small. It is only when eight or more wavelengths are used that the power gain becomes really significant, ie 6.3dBd for eight wavelengths. The angles (from the run of the antenna wire) at which radiation is at a maximum for different antenna lengths, together with the expected gain, are given in **Table 6.2**.

Wavelengths	Angle °	Gain dBd
1	54	0.5
1.5	42	0.9
2	36	1.3
2.5	33	1.8
3	30	2.2
4	26	3.0
5	22	4.0
6	20	4.8
7	19	5.5
8	18	6.3
9	17	6.9
10	16	7.5

Table 6.2 Gain of a long wire relative to a half-wave dipole.

In practice it will be found that the radiation from the end of the antenna which is furthest from the feed point is greater than that from the feed end. This is because the radiation lobes towards the far end are due to the forward-going wave along the wire, whereas from the feed end the radiation can only be due to the wave that is reflected from the far end. Loss by radiation together with any resistive losses will make the returning and reflected wave considerably weaker than the forward-going one. It is therefore best to direct long-wire antennas towards the preferred direction of radiation or reception.

USING COUNTERPOISE WIRES

End fed wires require to be operated with a good ground system. In an ideal world this would mean using a very short earth wire to a particularly good ground. This may not be a viable option in many instances, leading to even higher levels of RF in the vicinity of the station with all the attendant problems.

An upstairs shack can be particularly bedevilled by earthing problems, for often the run of the earth wire, even when made with heavy-gauge wire or flat strip, has a considerable inductance and will be long in terms of wavelength on the higher-frequency bands. When used for transmitting this could give rise to 'hot' equipment, a nasty phenomenon where supposedly earthed metal cases can give the operator an unpleasant RF burn when touched during transmission.

A method for reducing these effects is by using counterpoise wires connected to the ATU, although RF levels could still remain high. The arrangement shown in **Fig 6.3** at (a) is adequate for many situations (low power and receiving) and it includes an inductance L (with tap points) and a variable capacitor C, either of which may be used in series with the antenna wire to remove unwanted reactance at the feed point end of the wire. The jumper (J) will be used on those bands where reactance does not present a problem.

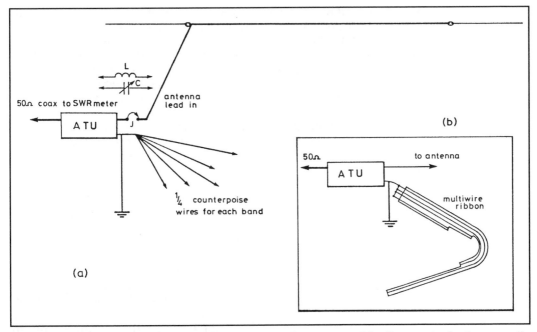

Fig 6.3 (a) A typical end-fed wire and counterpoise system. The 'jumper' wire is normally connected as shown but, if the antenna displays a capacitive or inductive reactance at certain frequencies, L or C can be inserted in series to cancel it out. (b) How a multi-wire ribbon cable can be cut to provide several quarter-wave counterpoise wires.

Reactance problems are usually revealed when it seems almost impossible to bring down the SWR between the ATU and the equipment to a sensible figure. It also may show as very sharp tuning of the ATU. A 'sensible' SWR reading means one which is something between unity and 1.5:1.

The counterpoise wires are cut to a quarter-wavelength for each band, and are best made with PVC covered multi-strand flexible wires. Such counterpoise wires will have a considerable RF voltage at their ends when the band they are cut for is in use and, if the output power is in excess of 50 watts, it is suggested that their ends are bent over and taped.

Counterpoise wires cut to the formula length seem to be effective but they can be set up more accurately with a dip oscillator. To do this, one end of the wire is connected to earth and at that end a half loop in the wire is loosely coupled to the dip oscillator coil. A receiver tuned to the wanted frequency, or better still a frequency counter coupled to the dip oscillator, will be more accurate than the calibration scale of the dip oscillator alone. If no dip oscillator is available three wires for each band could be used, two of these being cut either a few inches longer or shorter than the formula length.

Ribbon-cable counterpoises
A more elegant way to fabricate counterpoises for several wavebands is to use a length of multi-conductor ribbon cable. This cable is obtainable in 10-way format (or even 20- or 30-way). Such cable uses stranded

14 x 0.013mm tinned copper wires which are conveniently colour coded. The use of this ribbon as a four-band counterpoise is shown in Fig 6.3(b). A piece of ribbon is first cut to be a resonant quarter-wave on the lowest frequency band to be used, and it then has sections cut away to make quarter-wavelengths left behind for the remaining bands. Any spare wires can be used to 'broadband' the system by having additional wires that are a little longer or shorter than the calculated mid-band length.

It is best to splay out the end of each quarter-wave section for about 15cm (6in) to minimise possible flash-over problems at these points, especially when they are used in applications that allow the transmitter power to be high (more than 100 watts).

Counterpoises of this type do not contribute towards the radiation efficiency of the antenna, their purpose instead being to reduce or eliminate any RF feedback or matching problems. The 'earthy' ends of all the counterpoise wires must connect right to the earth connection on the ATU.

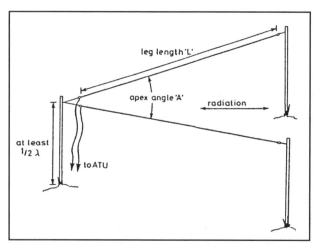

Fig 6.4 The simple V-beam which is bidirectional. If the apex of the 'V' is not far from the shack, two wires of equal length can be used as a twin-wire feeder. Their spacing is not important.

V-BEAMS

When two end-fed long wires are arranged as a horizontal 'V' and fed out of phase, they make a very effective bidirectional beam antenna that will work on several bands (see **Fig 6.4**). The feed to the 'V' can be of open-wire tuned line (or 300Ω ribbon used as a tuned line), or instead simply a pair of wires of equal length which come down to the ATU. These wires can be arranged to be spaced at any distance up to as much as about 2m (6ft) on the lower-frequency bands, and there will be no significant radiation from them. It is more usual to space the wires by around 15cm as described elsewhere. The apex angle of the 'V' is arranged so that the radiation lobes from each leg of the antenna reinforce each other within the 'V' and the outside lobes will cancel.

To get this reinforcement, and therefore the maximum gain, there are certain necessary criteria, the most important being the apex angle which depends upon the number of wavelengths contained in each leg of the antenna. The ideal apex angles for different leg lengths are given in **Table 6.3**.

Leg Length (wavelengths)	Apex Angle (Degrees °)
2	73
3	58
4	50
5	44
6	40
7	36
8	35

Table 6.3 Apex angles for various V-beam leg lengths.

It will be seen that the apex angle reduces by a smaller amount as the number of wavelengths increases, and this means that a compromise angle can be used which will provide useful gain over several bands. A V-beam with five-wavelength legs on 14MHz (about 106.6m or 350ft) will need an apex angle of 44°. This legs of this antenna will each be 7.5-wavelengths long on the 21MHz band and 10-wavelengths long on 28MHz. The optimum apex angles on 21 and 28MHz are 36 and 32° respectively, so a compromise angle of 35° will give an antenna which should work well on three bands. On 14MHz the vertical radiation angles will be raised from the very low angles obtainable when the apex angle is optimum but it will still be at or below 15° above the horizon.

Such an antenna can also be used on the 7 and 3.5MHz bands, although on these bands the gain is reduced and the vertical radiation angles will be higher. This is because the leg lengths are shorter in terms of wavelength and the apex angle is too small.

Gain and performance
The theoretical gain of a simple V-beam antenna which uses the correct apex angle is 3dB greater than the gain of a single wire as long as one leg of the 'V'. This means a gain of 7dBd for a five-wavelength V-beam. However, in practice the gain realised can be greater than this figure, because it is modified by the mutual impedance between the wires which make up the 'V', and is as much as an additional 1dB with a five-wavelength antenna. At eight-wavelengths per leg this additional gain will be almost 2dB, making a total gain for such an antenna as much as 11dBd.

Gain of this magnitude is very difficult to achieve with multi-element Yagi beams and represents a power gain of more than 10 times. Even more gain can be achieved by the stacking of two identical V-beams, one above the other, or by using two which are broadside to form a 'W'. However, such complexities put these varieties outside the scope of this book and are of more interest to commercial users.

The three supports which hold up the wires of a V-beam should be at least half a wavelength high at the lowest operating frequency. However, if such an antenna with supports at 11 to 12m (around 35 to 40ft), about a half-wavelength on 14MHz, is used on 7 and 3.5MHz, its performance on these bands will be similar to that of any horizontal antenna which is relatively close to the ground, and there will be mostly radiation at high angles.

Although leg lengths in terms of wavelength have been given for the determination of apex angles and antenna gain, the wires can be of any convenient length just as when single long wires are used. It is only important that both legs of the antenna are of equal length.

NON-RESONANT LONG WIRES
The simple end-fed long wire is a resonant device and it has standing waves along its length when in operation but, if such a wire is correctly terminated at its far end by the use of a suitable and non-inductive resistor, it becomes non-resonant and additionally unidirectional.

A single horizontal wire can be likened to one half of a two-wire transmission line, when the other wire has been replaced by the ground. The characteristic impedance of such a 'single-wire' transmission line, when using normal wire diameters and at a height of between 6 and 9m (around 20 to 30ft) will lie between 500 and 600Ω.

It was shown that the radiation away from the far end of a very long single-wire antenna resulted in a smaller proportion of the radiation being reflected back towards the feed point. If a resistor with a value equal to the characteristic impedance of the wire is fitted between the far end of the wire and ground (as shown in **Fig 6.5** at (a)), there will be little or no reflected wave. There will be a travelling wave along the wire but no

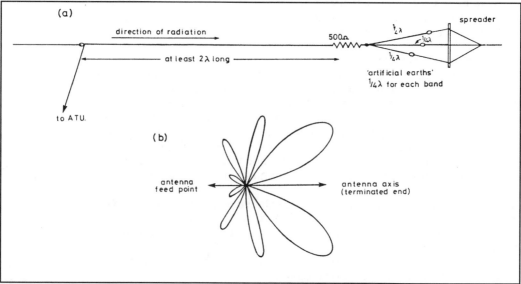

Fig 6.5 (a) A terminated end-fed wire which uses 'artificial' quarter-wave earth wires to terminate the 500 ohm non-inductive resistor. This antenna is shown for three-band use. (b) The horizontal radiation pattern of a typical terminated long-wire antenna showing its two main lobes.

standing waves, and the antenna will be similar to a correctly terminated transmission line but with one important difference - because of the very wide spacing between its conductors (the wire and the ground) it will radiate much of the energy applied at the feed point. Approximately half of the power will be dissipated by the terminating resistor but this is not important for the radiation is only needed in one direction.

There is the usual reciprocity and such an antenna has the same characteristics for both transmitting and receiving. The gain of a non-resonant wire is similar to that of a resonant wire of the same length so it is not useful unless it is at least two or more wavelengths long. The radiation pattern in the horizontal plane is similar to that of a resonant long wire but is modified by the unidirectional characteristic. Fig 6.5(b) shows the radiation pattern for a two-wavelength, non-resonant, terminated wire antenna. The angles of maximum radiation relative to the direction of the wire are almost the same as the angles for resonant wires. The antenna feed point will show an impedance of about 500Ω and this can be easily matched to a 50Ω equipment impedance by using a simple ATU of the L or pi section type.

A practical design

A most obvious problem when making an antenna of this type is the termination resistor's connection to earth. If the far end of the antenna was dropped to a resistor at ground level, there would then be about 9 to 12m (around 30 to 40ft) of vertical wire which would radiate in all directions and so ruin the unidirectional property of a non-resonant wire. If instead the resistor was left at the top and a wire was then taken down to ground, the wire would most certainly not be 'earthy' at its top end. The resistor would then present a reactive load to the antenna.

One way to overcome this problem is shown in Fig 6.5(a) where several quarter-wavelength wires are arranged to behave as 'artificial earths' for each frequency to be used. Only three such 'earths' are shown but these may be increased in number. Fig 6.5(a) shows the 500Ω resistor as an actual part of the antenna top with no indication as to how this may be arranged mechanically. The weight and tension of a long wire would damage any resistor fixed in the position shown in the diagram, so two alternatives are given in **Fig 6.6**. In (a) a rectangular insulating block is used both as antenna insulator and support for the resistors, and in (b) the insulating block with its resistors hangs beneath and is tied to a ribbed insulator.

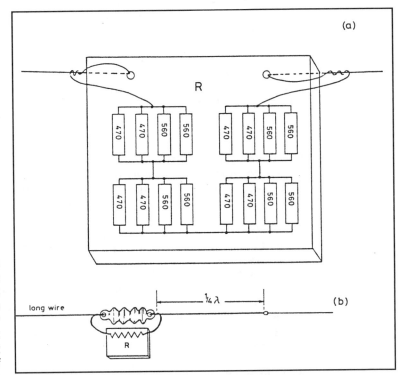

The resistor

The terminating resistor must be able to dissipate just under a half of the transmitter power which, when a basic 100-watt output transceiver is used (if methods can be determined to keep RF out of inhabited areas), will mean about 45W key-down.

Fig 6.6 (a) How a 32W non-inductive resistor of 500Ω resistance can be made up by using 16 individual 2W resistors in series-parallel. (b) The Perspex or similar mounting board for the resistors can also be used as an antenna insulator but, if a thinner material is employed, a separate conventional insulator may be used.

Fortunately the duty cycle in the CW mode is only about half of this, so a 25W resistor would in theory suffice. When using SSB, the duty cycle will depend upon how much processing is used. Some processors enable very high levels of duty cycle to be achieved and again a dissipation of 25W may be safe to assume. In practice it is best to have some margin in hand, and therefore a dissipation capability of an absolute minimum of 25W or 30 to 40W would be preferable.

High-wattage, non-inductive resistors are hard to locate and buy, so a suitable substitute can be constructed from several low-wattage components in a series / parallel combination. The arrangement shown in Fig 6.6(a) uses 16 carbon-film Hystab 2W resistors. The combination of 470Ω and 560Ω resistors will give an overall resistance of 510Ω and the power dissipation will be 32W. Whatever the type of resistor used it must be non-inductive and wire-wound types are therefore not suitable.

Protection against the weather is also essential when using resistors in an outside environment. One solution is to give the resistors and their connecting wires a liberal coating of clear silicone-rubber sealant. This was found to be very effective even in a location close to the sea, even though some forms of sealants were reputed to contain acetic acid that might attack the connections and wire over a long period of time. Similarly the heat dissipated by the resistors did not appear to damage or change the physical properties of the silicone rubber once it had stabilised and set. Another solution could be to house the resistors in a waterproof plastic container.

A NON-RESONANT V-BEAM

A standard V-antenna, made with a pair of equally long resonant wires, has a bi-directional radiation pattern. However, a V-beam can also be made with two terminated non-resonant wires and such a beam is unidirectional.

If only one support mast is used (at the feed end) the two wires may be sloped down to their terminating resistors at ground level. This greatly simplifies the construction of a V-beam, and it will have a maximum gain midway between the wires and in the direction away from the feed point.

A simplified drawing of the non-resonant V-beam is in **Fig 6.7**, where the leg lengths L must be a minimum of one wavelength long at its lowest operating frequency, and the mast height H should be between a half and three-quarters of the leg length. The apex angles for the different leg lengths are similar to those which are optimum for the resonant V-beams. Each terminating resistor has a value of 500Ω but, because the power is distributed equally between both wires, the power ratings of the resistors can be halved from what would be necessary when using a single terminated wire.

Being non-resonant, this V-antenna can be fed with a non-resonant feeder which should have a characteristic impedance of 500 to 600Ω. Such a feeder is easily made from 18SWG wires which are spaced 7.5mm (3in) apart, but any open-wire feeder or even 300Ω ribbon can be used instead as a tuned line. Another alternative would be to use a 9:1 step-up balun

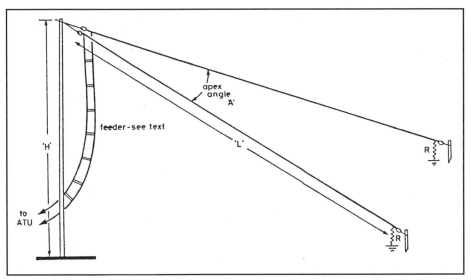

Fig 6.7 A terminated V-beam antenna. This is very useful for reliable point-to-point long-distance working. As the antenna wires tilt down to ground level their terminating resistors can connect to earth directly.

at the antenna apex which could then be connected to a 52Ω coaxial feeder. There would not be a perfect match, but the SWR would not be high and the losses would be insignificant.

This antenna will work over a frequency ratio of about 3:1 and give several decibels of gain across this range. Leg lengths of 30.5m (100ft) to give 1.5-wavelengths on 14MHz, with a support height of around 18m (60ft) and an apex angle of 80° will make a useful point-to-point antenna for long-distance work on the 14, 21 and 28MHz bands. The dimensions can be reduced to half-size (using the same apex angle) for operation on 28 and 50MHz, making a compact antenna to fit into most average sized gardens.

Quarter wave 'artificial earths' are not needed for this design because the ends descend to ground level. However, it should be remembered that the earth system for the terminated ends should not be neglected as they form an essential part of the radiating system. Not only should a DC connection be provided (for safety as well as the RF performance), but a radial system should also be considered. A system of six radials, each extending out for between 11 and 12m would ensure that the performance of the earth is satisfactory.

THE W3EDP ANTENNA

The W3EDP antenna is a simple yet effective multi-band design that has been around for many years. It uses a 25.9m (85ft) wire with a 5.1m (17ft) counterpoise connected when used on some bands. It is found that the antenna wire itself may be bent to suit typical suburban locations without any marked degradation in performance.

The W3EDP antenna is shown in **Fig 6.8** and looks something like an end-fed Zepp with a 20.7m (68ft) top and a 5.2m (17ft) feed line. The feeder is rather unusual in that the wires which make it up need not be parallel. The counterpoise (half the feeder line) can be run outside in any direction.

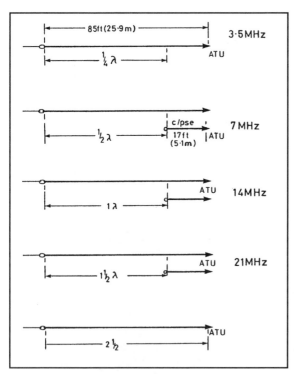

Figure 6.8 The 85ft W3EDP single-wire antenna will behave rather like an end-fed Zepp on 7, 14 and 21MHz. The counterpoise wire, although not positioned close to the antenna, will nevertheless act like one wire of an open-wire Zepp feed system.

Five-band working

On 3.5MHz the counterpoise is not connected and the antenna behaves as an end-fed wire about 5.8m (19ft) longer than an electrical quarter-wave. An advantage here is that the point of maximum radiation (the high current point) is almost 6m (20ft) along the wire. This additional length from the basic quarter-wave also ensures that the impedance at the lower feed point end is not too low, so there will be easier matching to the ATU with some inductive reactance which can easily be tuned out.

The counterpoise is connected for operation on 7MHz and the antenna becomes a half-wave with a wide spaced 'feeder' which is about an eighth-wavelength long. At the feed point the impedance will not be very high, nor will it show the very low impedance (approximately 36Ω) that is present a quarter of a wavelength from the end of a half-wavelength top. Instead there is a medium impedance which can be matched without difficulty.

On 14MHz the antenna wire is within a few centimetres of being a resonant full-wavelength for this band, and the 'feeder' is just 15cm longer than an electrical quarter-wavelength. The impedance at the ATU end is low, but not so low as it might be were the 'feeder' an exact quarter-wavelength.

On 21MHz the antenna wire now becomes almost a full wavelength and a half. The high impedance at the shack end of this 1.5-wave section connects to the final 5.6m (17ft) which then becomes a part of the feeder which is about 3/8-wavelength long. This length presents a medium impedance at the feed point and is easy to match.

The counterpoise is not required when the antenna used on 28MHz so the antenna then behaves as a 2.5-wavelength end-fed wire. This band is the only one where there may be matching problems, for the feed end of 2.5-wavelength wire is at quite a high impedance. The introduction of a series capacitor between the antenna and the ATU might help to reduce matching problems for it will electrically shorten the antenna.

The W3EDP is perhaps one of the simplest and cheapest of all multi-band antennas, being simple and inexpensive to construct and then easy to install. As a result it is a favourite with some of the QRP fraternity, and with just a few watts it is easy to obtain contacts over reasonable distances on all the bands on which it will operate.

THE G8ON ANTENNA

This end fed wire antenna was first described by Harold Chadwick, G8ON, for DX working on the 1.8MHz band (3.5MHz versions could also be made) in the September 1957 issue of the *RSGB Bulletin*, and this was followed by a second article in June 1966. The antenna placed the current maximum in the vertical section remote and thereby enabling the low angle radiation required for long distance work. It also gave a significant level of ground wave ideal for local work at these frequencies as well. Other antennas for these frequencies often have the current maximum in the horizontal section and this results in high angle radiation, the antenna performing in a similar manner to a low dipole.

The original G8ON antenna is shown in **Fig 6.9** at (a). The wires B, C and D are arranged to be a half-wavelength in total at the intended lowest operating frequency, with the vertical portion C being as long as is possible. This vertical section should be at least 2m (6ft) from a metal mast and this preferably should be insulated from the ground. A short single-wire feeder A is used to ease the matching at the ATU. This is small in terms of wavelength and will have little effect on antenna performance. The two wire lengths Band D are at opposite potential, and are virtually the opposite plates of a capacitor which is shorted by the inductance C.

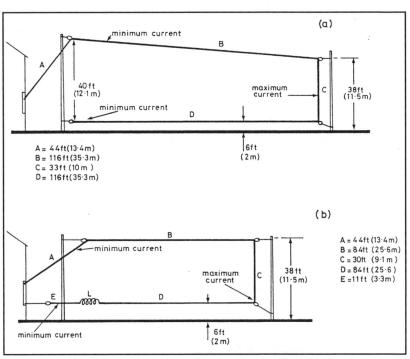

Fig 6.9 (a) The original G8ON 1.8MHz antenna. The maximum current will be several feet up from the bottom of the vertical section. (b) This later (1966) version of the G8ON antenna uses a loading coil 11ft from the end of the wire. The electrical centre and the point of maximum current is at the foot of the vertical section. Earthing the wire here and removing D, E and L would in no way alter the performance of this antenna.

This means that a displacement current will flow in the air dielectric between the horizontal wires.

The version illustrated in Fig 6.9 (b) may be used in shorter gardens. The length from the end point E to C at the centre of the vertical wire must be a quarter-wavelength on the lowest operating frequency. It is suggested that the wire E should be at least 3.3m (11ft) long. This arrangement tends to reduce the displacement current but it can still be very effective. When used at twice the design frequency (as a full-wave wire) the antenna currents in the horizontal wires will be in phase, and so operate as two half-waves in phase. This will give some gain at right angles to the run of the antenna.

In order to determine the correct inductance of L, it must be adjusted to give the maximum RF current in the vertical wire C. A small lamp or RF current meter can be inserted in the centre of C and the number of turns on the coil L may be varied to give maximum current.

It has been found that the presence of sandy soil or a poor earth system does not reduce the efficiency of this antenna. This might be because the wire D is only about 2m (6ft) above ground. Sandy soil and sub-soil will mean that the true earth will be many feet below the surface, and so the operation of the antenna will be enhanced.

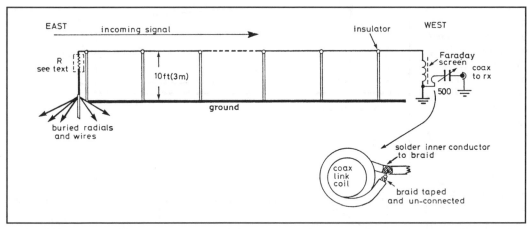

Fig 6.10 The terminated Beverage receiving antenna for use on 1.8 or 3.5MHz. The Faraday screen is made from one or two turns of coaxial cable. To be effective a Beverage antenna must be at least one wavelength long.

BEVERAGE ANTENNAS
The Beverage antenna is the probably the best known version of what is termed a 'Wave Antenna'. It is used by many 160m enthusiasts because it enables weak signals to be received with lower levels of noise than many other antennas, including directional loops on this band. Although excellent for receiving, the antenna is very inefficient and therefore not used for transmitting.

The antenna consists of a length of wire longer than a wavelength supported at a low level, typically around 3m or 10 ft above ground, and terminated at the far end in a resistor with the same value as the characteristic impedance of the antenna (**Fig 6.10**).

The wave antenna is most responsive to signals that have a very low angle of reception that maintain a constant vertical polarisation. These conditions do not normally exist on many signals received at high frequencies, and therefore the Beverage antenna is seldom used on these frequencies. However, for the 160 and 80m bands long haul signals are often present with these characteristics and this makes the Beverage such an ideal antenna for those who have the space to erect one.

In operation the Beverage antenna acts like a long transmission line with one lossy conductor and one good conductor. The good conductor is the antenna wire whereas the lossy conductor is the earth. In Fig 6.9 a Beverage antenna is shown running along a line from east to west and a transmitting station is assumed to lie to the east. The travelling wave from this station, when it reaches the antenna wire, will move along it from east to west and induce currents in the wire which then travel in both directions.

The current travelling east moves against the motion of the wave and it reduces to almost zero when the wire is one wavelength or more long. The currents travelling west, however, travel at almost the velocity of light and will therefore move along with the wave. These currents moving west all add up in phase at the west end and produce a strong signal there.

If the eastern end of the wire was either grounded or open-circuit, the induced currents generated by signals from either the east or the west would be reflected back to the western end of the wire. The antenna would then become bidirectional.

The terminating resistor R absorbs the RF energy reaching the far end of the wire, so preventing any reflection, and gives the antenna a unidirectional property. The resistance of R must match the surge impedance of the antenna wire, and this depends upon both the thickness of the wire and its height above the ground. It usually has a resistance of between 200 and 400Ω and must be non-inductive.

A Beverage works best over a *poor* earth but the earthing to which the terminating resistor connects must be very good. Several radials or buried wires should therefore be used. A simple transformer steps down the high impedance of the Beverage wire to a low value which is suitable for a match to a coaxial cable. The secondary of this transformer should be electrostatically shielded from the primary winding, and this is easily managed by the use of a two (or more) turn link winding made at the end of the coaxial cable. This is arranged as a Faraday screen.

Length and performance
One wavelength must be regarded as a minimum length for an effective Beverage antenna, and on 1.8MHz this will be about 160m or 500ft.

Single-wire Beverages have an optimum length of from one to three wavelengths and an optimum height above ground of 3 and 6m (approximately 10 to 20ft).

A terminated Beverage gives strong signals from stations that are located away from its far end, and will have almost no pick-up at all from its sides. It also has a very low noise level with a considerable attenuation of atmospheric noise. There is no other antenna type its equal for the reception of DX on the 1.8MHz amateur band. Loops are good but are really not in the same class as a Beverage wave antenna.

Unfortunately point-to-point working is not often very important to amateurs, for they generally wish to contact different distant stations which may be located anywhere in the world - several Beverage antennas would be needed to do this. Few amateur operators are fortunate enough to have the ground which is needed to set up one or more Beverage antennas, so most workers on the LF bands must use other low-noise systems.

G3NCN 'SKYMISER' ANTENNA

This antenna was first described by John Ellerton, G3NCN, in the June 1999 issue of *RadCom*. It offers a design for a 160m antenna that can fit into an average garden.

The basic configuration for the antenna is shown in **Fig 6.11.** It consists of a vertical section, fed at the top by a horizontal wire and the whole antenna is tuned by a conventional tuning arrangement. There is no complex high-Q matching unit, and no single band solution. The antenna is simple to construct and will operate on all bands, but it only operates as a reasonably true vertical on 1.8MHz and possibly on 3.5MHz. It is left to the antenna experts to calculate the theoretical performance. Although the design is simple and the antenna itself is easy to erect, the performance is dependent upon the use of an efficient earthing arrangement. Ideas mentioned in Chapter 1 can be implemented to ensure a good arrangement is adopted.

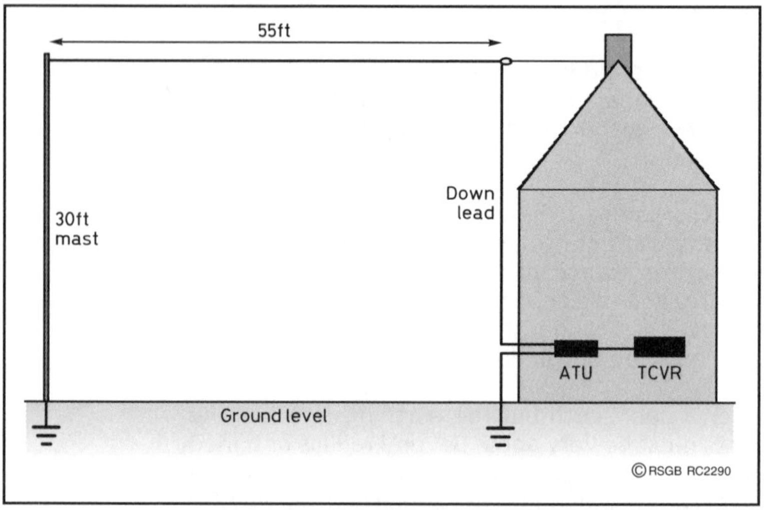

Figure 6.11 Basic arrangement for the Skymiser antenna.

The antenna is electrically continuous from the base of the mast to the shack. The horizontal wire connected to the top of the mast as shown in

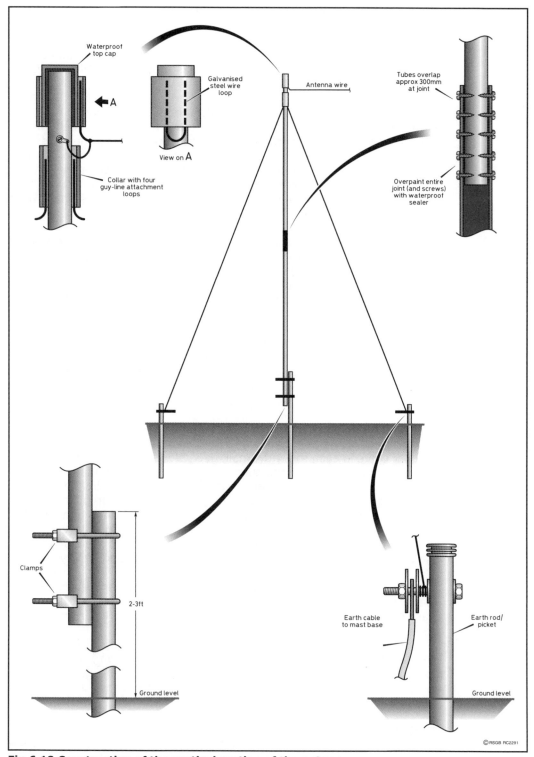

Fig 6.12 Construction of the vertical section of the antenna.

Fig 6.12. At the base of the mast and at the shack there are independent earth systems.

At the base of the mast the antenna is fastened by two TV antenna-type clamps to a 50mm (2in) diameter stub mast about 1.6m (5ft) long, 1m (3ft) of which is driven into the ground.

The mast itself consists of two 5m (15ft) lengths of aluminium tube, the larger of which is 50mm diameter. The other length fits closely inside. The diameters are not critical, but the close fit of one tube inside the other is. The mast sections were obtained from a non-ferrous metal stockist. An overlap of about 300mm should be provided at the joint of the two sections, then the sections should be drilled and secured with self tapping screws (three rows of 5 screws, 120 degrees apart were used in the prototype).

At the top of the mast a cap of fibreglass matting and epoxy resin is employed to keep out the rain. When this has hardened, a half loop of galvanised (coat hanger) wire is formed and laid next to the cap. A collar of fibreglass matting is wound around the half loop and the cap, to secure it to the mast head, then soaked in epoxy resin by stippling with a brush. The top section of the antenna will be fastened to this loop.

A second collar of fibreglass matting and resin is constructed just below the cap. Once it has cured, four half loops of galvanised wire are placed on top of it and bound into place with a second layer of fibreglass matting, then soaked in epoxy resin (as per the cap). Guy lines will be fastened to these loops.

The earth rods (which double as pickets) are driven into the ground using a club hammer. The tubing may be expected to fold as it is driven into the ground. Drive in each rod with small, even blows, and an even number of times around the top of the tube. Every few inches, remove the tube from the ground and remove any earth from inside the tube. Then return it to the ground and continue driving gently until the top of the tube is about 6in above the ground. Remove the rod one last time, and also drill transverse holes through it at 6in intervals below ground level. Return the rods to the ground. Water can then be poured down the pipe to keep the area surrounding it moist and thereby improve conductivity.

The guy lines - made from garden line - and earthing cables are fixed to the earth rods using stainless steel nuts, bolts and washers. All the fittings were purchased from a local do-it-yourself hardware dealer and should be available quite freely.

This antenna is a true 'plumber's delight' construction. There are no complicated matching units at the base of the vertical and all controls are in the hands of the operator, so that changing frequency is as easy as tuning a long wire antenna.

Tuning
Tuning is accomplished by an ATU located in the shack. On some frequencies the feed impedance is high - especially on 1.8MHz where the

length of the antenna approaches a quarter-wavelength, and also to some extent on 3.5MHz. To accommodate this, a special ATU was developed for the tuning task on those bands. For other bands an MFJ tuner was used although many other types would suffice. The overall arrangement for tuning is shown in **Fig 6.13**.

When the commercially made ATU is used to tune the antenna, its output is connected directly to the antenna wire via S1, and the ATU is used with tuning elements selected. When connected for 1.8MHz, the antenna is connected to the top of the 'tank circuit' and the commercial tuner (connected to the coil tap) is used without tuning elements. The VSWR meter of the ATU serves to indicate correct tuning in all cases.

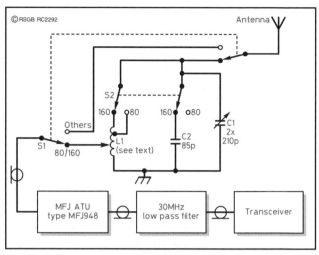

Fig 6.13 Tuning is accomplished on 1.8 and 3.5MHz using a home-made tuner. On the other bands a commercially made (MFJ) tuner was used.

The coil (L1) used for the home constructed part of the tuning was an ex-transmitter tank tuning coil. Its diameter was 90mm, its length 170mm. and it had 29 turns. The tap was set by rotating a 'finger' inside the coil which selected the appropriate turn for the tap. This is not wholly necessary since the tapping point could be achieved by soldering a piece of wire on to the appropriate turn of a similar coil. The tuning capacitor (C1) was an ex-service wide spaced twin gang (2 x 210pF). For 3.5MHz it was used alone and for 1.8MHz it was used in parallel with a high voltage 85pF fixed capacitor C2. For 1.8MHz the whole coil was used for tuning, and for 3.5MHz the top of the coil was at 22 turns from the earthy end.

Horizontal section and down lead
The horizontal wire and down lead are made from twisting together 10 strands of 30SWG enamelled wire, which was fastened to a nail at one end. The other was clamped in a hand drill to effect the twisting action. The end connected to the mast top is mechanically tied to the mast, then the wire, terminated in a ring tag, is looped and the ring tag bolted to the masthead. This relieves strain on the electrical connection.

All connections of wire to the mast and between mast sections are painted with sealing paint of the kind used to make roofs waterproof. The horizontal antenna wire down lead is multi-stranded to reduce resistance due to RF skin effect.

Current distribution
The diagrams of current distribution shown in **Fig 6.14** are imagined for 1.8. 3.5 and 7MHz. Although rigorously proved,

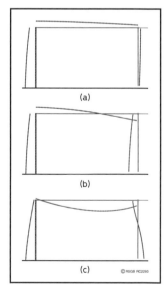

Fig 6.14 Imagined current distribution for (a) 1.8 MHz (b) 3.5MHz and (c) 7MHz.

the performance of the antenna tends to support the distributions shown in the diagrams.

On 1.8MHz the antenna behaves as a top-fed vertical. Radiation tends to be omni-directional, although currents in the horizontal section and feed wire undoubtedly modify that. Similar behaviour is expected on 3.5MHz although modification of the omni-directional characteristic will be greater and some useful horizontally polarised radiation helps in more local operation. Because the length of the overall mast and wire combination is significantly less than a half-wavelength, the feed point impedance is high and it needs the special tuning arrangement similar to 1.8MHz.

On 7MHz the vertical feed wire and the mast team up to emulate two verticals out of phase. Results obtained from using the antenna support this idea. The antenna gives good results along the alignment of the mast and down lead. Some radiation is also expected from the top section, but this is higher angle.

Modifying the length of the top to be 66ft and the masts to be 33ft long can be expected to enhance the phased vertical behaviour on 7MHz and increase the gain along the direction of the axis of the mast down lead. On 3.5MHz the feed impedance should become lower and the commercial tuner would more likely be used for tuning. On 1.8MHz the special tuning unit will be necessary more than ever because the feed impedance is expected to rise as the length becomes closer to quarter-wavelength.

Chapter 7
Vertical Antennas

There is a large variety of antennas that are essential vertical antennas. These antennas have a number of advantages that they are easy to fit into a small garden while also being able to offer a low angle of radiation required for long distance communication. This is provided they are not screened too much by local objects. Nevertheless these antennas provide an ideal solution for many who have limited space.

The most basic vertical antenna is the quarter-wave antenna. In this configuration one connection from the feeder is taken to the quarter-wave vertical radiating element, and the other is taken to ground. In this way the ground provides the 'image', or other half of the antenna as shown in **Fig 7.1** at (a). As such the ground connection is an integral part

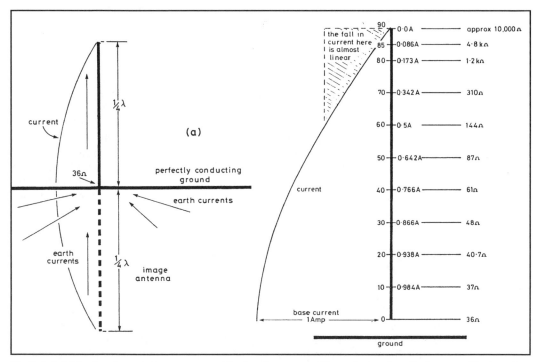

Fig 7.1 (a) The basic quarter-wave vertical antenna positioned over 'perfect ground', showing its earth image. Most of the earth return currents flow through the ground in the vicinity of the antenna. (b) A representation of a quarter-wave vertical antenna over perfect ground which is energised by 36W of power. The RF current at 10° points along its length is shown and also the impedance at these points. There is a rapid fall in current towards the top of the antenna and the impedance therefore rises greatly there. It is interesting to note that the fall in current over the final 30° of this antenna is almost linear.

of the antenna system as a whole, and upon its effectiveness rests the efficiency of the whole antenna. In fact this is true for any antenna of this nature that uses the ground for one of its connections.

In view of the fact that one of the connections from the feeder is taken to ground, this type of antenna is an unbalanced antenna. Accordingly it can be fed directly using unbalanced feeder, such as coax, without the need for a balun.

The impedance at the point where a resonant quarter-wavelength vertical conductor meets the ground is about 36Ω - just a half of the feed impedance at the centre of a resonant half-wave dipole. The current along the quarter-wave vertical antenna is at its maximum at its base and therefore the greatest radiation will take place at this point (see Fig 7.1 (b)). The radiation will be vertically polarised and in the example illustrated will have equal field-strength levels in all directions.

Much of its radiation will be at low angles to the horizon when above a good ground, and this makes the vertical antenna very attractive for both short-distance (ground wave) and long-distance communications on the lower-frequency bands. The polarisation of an antenna when used for long-distance work does not matter, for the effects of refraction in the ionosphere etc will inevitably induce changes in polarisation.

In order to be able to gain the most from a vertical antenna, the ground system that is used with it must be efficient. The ideal is a mat of buried wire extending to at least a quarter-wavelength and possibly a half-wavelength from the base of the antenna as discussed in Chapter 1. For most practical situations this may not be possible and these antennas will still work with a good DC ground and at least one buried quarter-wavelength radial for the band of operation. It is also possible to use a raised ground plane system, and some of the commercially manufactured trap vertical antennas used shortened ground plane systems consisting of a single trapped counterpoise. Although not as effective as a full ground plane, they are able to operate satisfactorily and enable a vertical antenna to be erected and operated when it might otherwise not be possible. They also allow the antenna to be raised in height allowing them to take advantage of the 'height gain' available.

Although apparently simple in concept, the vertical antenna presents some design problems if it is to be an efficient radiator when shortened for operation on the low bands. For example, it can be calculated that a 'short' vertical antenna used on 1.8MHz, such as a 4.2m (14ft), 0.03-wavelength, bottom-loaded wire or rod used over a poor ground system having an earth resistance of about 100Ω, will have a radiating efficiency of only 0.26%. This means that a power of 8W into such an antenna will result in only 20mW being actually radiated. The other 7.98W will be dissipated as heat in the ground resistance and in the resistance of its loading coil.

Fig 7.1 (a) represents a simplified and 'ideal' quarter-wave vertical antenna. The ground is shown to be a perfect conducting medium, a condition which can only be realised when it is replaced by a sheet of metal which has dimensions that are large relative to the length of the antenna (or less effectively by a large area of salt water). The ground, if it is a perfect conductor, will behave like an electrostatic shield and provide an 'image' antenna a quarter-wave below the radiator. This image completes the missing half of a half-wave antenna, and earth return currents will be induced in the ground.

PRACTICAL ARRANGEMENTS

It is seldom possible or convenient to erect a full-sized quarter-wave vertical for the lower-frequency bands, although such antennas are often used on the higher frequencies. For the lower frequency bands it is often necessary to look at ways of physically reducing their length. In **Fig 7.2**, at (a) the quarter-wave is in the vertical plane and is shown to be bottom fed (impedance 36Ω). Figs 7.2 (b), (c) and (d) show reducing lengths of the vertical antenna sections and corresponding increases in the lengths of the horizontal components. The total height of the antenna is therefore lowered and in (d), where only 25% of the quarter-wave is vertical, the antenna is only 0.06-wavelength above ground.

The three 'bent' quarter-wave antennas shown in (b), (c) and (d) are often called 'inverted-L' antennas, and they are very popular arrangements when mast height is limited. As the vertical part of an inverted-L is reduced in length, the proportion of the radiated power at low angles and in the vertical plane also diminishes. The horizontal top section will then contribute more of the total radiation, this radiation being horizontally polarised and at high angles to the horizon. This high-angle radiation is a result of the antenna being close to the ground.

An inverted-L similar to that shown at (c), where the vertical and horizontal portions are

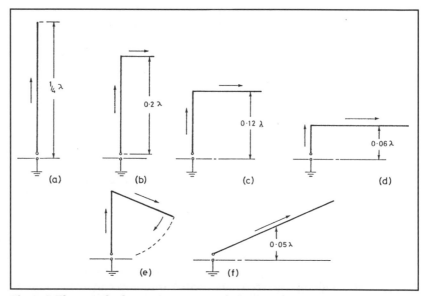

Fig 7.2 The vertical quarter-wave can have a proportion of its length bent horizontally as shown in (b), (c) and (d). When this is done the antenna is usually called an 'inverted-L'. As the proportion of the vertical section falls the vertically polarised radiation at low angles also falls, the horizontal top giving horizontally polarised high-angle radiation. The example shown at (d) will have most of its radiation at very high angles and will only be suitable for short to medium distance working. It will also have a much reduced ground wave. Bending the top of the inverted-L down will mean that the antenna currents in the two sections will then tend to be out of phase and begin to cancel. At (f) the sloping wire will behave almost like a length of unterminated open-wire feeder.

equal in length, should give useful vertically polarised radiation at low angles for both DX work and also 'local' working within the ground wave range. The high-angle radiation from its top horizontal half will be effective for short range communications.

In Fig 7.2 (e) the top half of the quarter-wave is dropped down towards the ground. This will reduce both the radiation from the vertical section and also from the sloping part of the antenna, as the RF currents in the two sections will be partly in opposition. In (f) there is both vertically and horizontally polarised radiation, in proportion according to the slope of the antenna. The sloping wire, even halfway along its length, is only 0.05-wavelength above ground. This antenna will tend to behave as a lossy transmission line, having the ground as a conductor, and any radiation will be at high angles. There will also be very little ground wave, so such an arrangement will be poor both for local working or for DX.

Another feature of inverted-L antennas is that they tend to radiate most strongly in the direction away from the 'elbow'. This directivity can sometimes be useful when particular countries or continents are the radiation 'targets'.

All the antennas shown in Fig 7.2 are full-sized, quarter-wave types and they will have a base feed impedance of around 36Ω at resonance. As a result it is quite acceptable to feed the antenna with 50Ω coax as the match will be sufficiently close. Even if the earth had zero resistance so that the actual feed impedance seen in practice was 36Ω this would only result in an SWR of 1.4:1. With even a small earth resistance the actual feed impedance seen is likely to be closer to 50Ω.

BASE LOADING AND TOP LOADING

Quarter-wave antennas can be reduced in physical length and will still radiate if properly loaded to resonance. There are two commonly used types of loading: bottom loading and top loading. There is also centre loading as an intermediate form, but this can be difficult to arrange, an important exception being in the design of very short antennas for

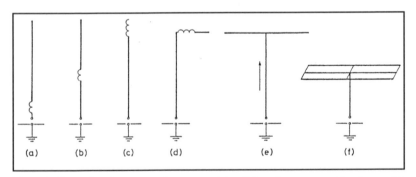

Fig 7.3 Short (under a quarter-wavelength) antennas can be brought to electrical resonance by either bottom loading (a), centre loading (b) or top loading (c) using some inductance in series. By having the loading inductance a little way down from the top of the antenna, as shown at (d), there is a reduced likelihood of corona discharges and the inductance can also be smaller. The 'T' antenna at (e) is an example of top loading, and the fact that the currents in each leg of the top are anti-phase will mean that there will be little radiation from the top. An increased amount of top-loading capacitance as shown in (f) will allow quarter-wave resonance to be obtained with a shorter vertical section.

mobile operations. Centre loading is rarely used with fixed-station antennas. The arrangement shown in **Fig 7.3** at (a) is a typical example of base loading. The inductance is at the bottom end of the antenna and it makes up the length deficiency of the radiator.

Unfortunately base loading is the least efficient method and it lowers the radiation resistance of the antenna. The maximum radiation from a quarter-wave antenna is at its high-current point, and when base loading is used this will be along the loading coil. Furthermore any inductor used for loading will have a certain resistance and this will introduce losses as heat is dissipated. This is particularly important in the high current end of the antenna, ie at the base, and therefore thick wire must be used. It is all the more important because an inductor for base loading will generally be made with a length of wire which is about twice the 'missing' length of the antenna.

Fig 7.3 (b) shows the centre-loading coil arrangement and at (c) an inductor top loads the antenna. This method is seldom used as shown because the inductance must be quite large, and the very high RF voltages generated at its top end may induce corona discharges unless special precautions are taken to stop this.

Fig 7.3 (d) shows a combination of both inductive top loading and some additional capacitance. Extra capacitance at the top of an antenna will allow the use of a much smaller top-loading coil. At (e) the top-loading arrangement uses just additional capacitance and does not have an inductor. This type of antenna is often described as a 'T' and it is frequently made from a centre-fed antenna which has both its feeder wires 'strapped' together at the bottom. The G5RV or tuned-doublet antenna used in this way can become a useful vertical antenna if tuned against a good ground system.

By employing more top capacitance the vertical section of the antenna may be further reduced in length, as seen in (f). Here a multi-wire, top-loading capacitance is shown. Similar arrangements used with either 'T' or inverted-L antennas have long associations with ship-borne radio installations where there are obvious antenna length restrictions for LF work.

The RF currents in the two horizontal wires at the top of a 'T' antenna are in anti-phase, and therefore there will not be much radiation from them in the horizontal plane. Any radiation there is will tend to be at right angles to the line of the wires making up the top. For a more complete suppression of the horizontal component, another pair of wires should be run out at the junction of the 'T' but at right angles to the other two top wires. This can be arranged by drooping slightly the top-loading wires with little loss in the efficiency of the vertical section.

EFFICIENCY

The antenna efficiency is an important issue with grounded antennas. As the earth system forms part of the antenna system as a whole its performance has a major affect on the overall performance. A high earth resistance will dissipate power that would otherwise be radiated. Accordingly it is necessary to have a view of the overall antenna efficiency.

The power supplied to a quarter-wave antenna is dissipated in three main ways. The first is the radiation resistance, where power is converted into electromagnetic energy and radiated. However, it is also dissipated in the ground resistance, and the resistance of the antenna radiating element including any inductors placed within it. Of the losses the ground resistance is likely to be the greatest, although the conductor resistance should not be neglected.

It is possible to calculate the antenna efficiency. I is equal to the power radiated divided by the power supplied, and can be defined as the ratio of the radiation resistance to the total antenna system resistance:

Efficiency = $\dfrac{\text{Radiation resistance} \times 100\%}{(\text{Radiation resistance} + \text{Loss resistances})}$

It can be seen that the antenna efficiency can only be 100% when the ground resistance and resistive antenna resistances are zero. This is obviously impossible, but figures may begin to approach 100% in the case of an antenna made from thick low resistance conductor wire or tube situated over an almost perfect conducting plane (or sea water).

Unfortunately as a vertical is loaded to shorten it, so the value of its radiation resistance falls and the other resistance losses become more significant. In defining the length of the antenna relative to a wavelength the number of degrees is often used. Thus a full wavelength is 360° and a quarter-wavelength is 90°. For top loaded verticals, the efficiency only drops off seriously when the antenna's vertical length is below 35° (0.1-wavelength), and fortunately on the 1.8MHz band this length can be achieved when using a 15m (50ft) support mast. When using base loading the situation is a little worse where the efficiency of a 35° vertical falls to only 24%, and the very short 10° (about 5m or 15ft for 1.8MHz) antenna becomes only 2.4% efficient.

The radiation resistance of short vertical antennas is given in **Table 7.1**.

These figures indicate the importance of a investing in as good an earth system as possible along with ensuring that the losses in the radiating antenna conductor with its loading coil are reduced to the minimum. It is for this reason that large loading coils with thick wire are often seen on vertical antennas.

THE FOLDED VERTICAL ANTENNA
One of the problems with an ordinary vertical antenna is the relatively low radiation resistance that can lead to low values of efficiency, especially when the earth connection is poor. This can be overcome to a degree by using a folded vertical antenna. By using a length of 300Ω ribbon as a 'half-folded dipole' or 'folded unipole', the radiation resistance of the antenna is raised to a value in the region of 80 -150Ω, depending on configuration and height. This means that even when used with an average earth system the antenna will have an efficiency of around 40%.

The version described here uses a shortened 300Ω ribbon section to which is added a length of single wire. To calculate the length of the ribbon needed, an electrical quarter-wavelength at the desired frequency must be multiplied by the velocity factor of the ribbon used (slotted ribbon has a velocity factor of 0.87). This length is less than a quarter-wave, and it must have an additional wire connected at its end to make it up to be an electrical quarter-wavelength. This technique is very similar to that used when constructing folded half-wave dipoles from 300Ω ribbon (see Chapter 3).

Height as a proportion of a wavelength(°)	Base loaded (ohms)	Top loaded (ohms)
90	36	36
85	30.2	35.7
80	25.3	34.9
75	21.1	33.5
70	17.65	31.78
65	14.61	29.57
60	12.0	27.0
55	9.75	24.15
50	7.82	21.12
45	6.17	18.0
40	4.76	14.87
35	3.57	11.84
30	2.58	9.0
25	1.76	6.42
20	1.11	4.21
15	0.62	2.41
10	0.27	1.08
5	0.06	0.27

Table 7.1 Radiation resistance of short vertical antennas according to W J Byron, W7DHD (90° = quarter-wavelength).

The folded antenna illustrated in **Fig 7.4** is designed for 3.7MHz operation and it only needs 10.6m (35ft) high supports. The efficiency of the antenna is proportionally higher than a single wire vertical because the length of its vertical section is increased as a proportion of the total quarter-wavelength. Six buried radial wires, each being at least a quarter-wavelength long, are recommended for a suitable earth system, although with the limitations of many garden plots this may not be achievable and at

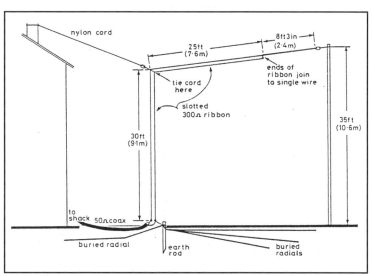

Fig 7.4 The folded vertical antenna which uses 300Ω ribbon for most of its length. The use of the 'folded dipole' principle raises the feed impedance of this antenna from around 15Ω to four times this figure. A reasonable match can be obtained with 50Ω coaxial feeder.

least one quarter-wavelength buried radial with a good selection of earth rods and the like may have to suffice. Versions of this antenna may be scaled up or down for use on other bands.

The step-up of feed impedance brought about by using this folded dipole technique allows the use of a 50Ω coaxial feeder. The greater distance between the vertical part of this antenna and any buildings etc, the more effective the antenna will be for low-angle long-distance communication.

QUARTER-WAVE SLOPERS

Sloper antennas have become popular as low-band antennas that can be erected alongside an HF beam on a tower. Although sloping dipoles as described in Chapter 3 are very similar, these slopers comprise a single section and are usually classed as a form of vertical antenna. They provide some directivity and can be erected very easily, making them an ideal antenna for many stations.

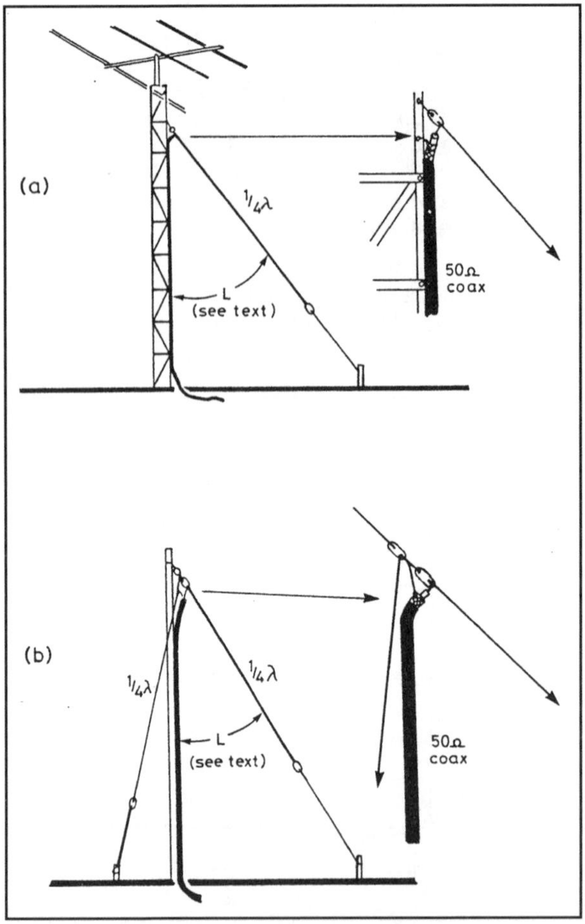

Fig 7.5 (a) A quarter-wave sloper antenna used with a metal tower. (b) Using a quarter-wavelength of wire which is almost vertical to replace the metal tower. The feed impedance of the sloper depends upon several variables, one being the angle L.

The quarter-wave or 'half-sloper' antenna is really half of an inverted-V dipole. A quarter-wave antenna is normally arranged to be bottom-fed, which means that the maximum radiation is at the base of the antenna. By inverting the feed point of a quarter-wave as shown in **Fig 7.5** at (a), the position of the current maximum and therefore the greatest radiation can be moved to the top of the antenna.

The 'ground' against which slopers are fed is usually the metallic mass of the support tower, although for this to be as efficient as possible, a good low resistance ground at the foot of the tower remains important. The slope angle L of a half-sloper is usually 45°, and its maximum radiation is in the direction of the wire away from its feed point. The gain of a sloper is said to be between 3 and 6dB over a half-wave dipole but this depends upon the quality of the earth system below. Buried radials or earth mats etc are needed if the best results are to be realised.

The feed impedance of the sloper depends on a variety of factors. For a start, the feed impedance of a quarter-wave antenna is normally about 36Ω but a quarter-wave sloper antenna can have a feed impedance which may lie anywhere between 30 and 60Ω. The actual impedance depends upon three variables: the length of the wire; the tower or mast height; and the enclosed angle between the wire and its support.

If a metal tower is used this becomes a part of the resonant system and there will be a voltage maximum somewhere between the antenna feed point and ground. Any other antennas, such as beams, which may be located on top of the support tower will also influence the feed impedance and the antenna's performance. Any guy wires which support the tower must be made non-resonant by breaking them into suitable lengths with insulators.

The version as shown in Fig 7.5(b) uses a non-metallic support mast, and it has an additional quarter-wavelength of wire which effectively forms the missing half of the dipole. This should drop vertically or almost vertically down towards the ground. If the feeder SWR is high it can often be brought down to an acceptable figure by changing the wire slope angle. It should be possible to bring the SWR down to a level of 1.5:1 or better.

It is possible to make an all-band version of the half-sloper. This cannot be achieved when using 50Ω coaxial feed, so instead an open-wire line (Zepp feed) to an ATU is suggested. The measured bandwidths of half-slopers are about 50kHz at 1.8MHz, 100kHz at 3.6MHz, 200kHz at 7 MHz and so on, becoming progressively greater as the frequency increases. A quarter-wave sloper antenna, when designed for operation around 1830kHz can therefore have a rather high SWR when used above 1.9MHz.

A THREE-WIRE SLOPING ANTENNA
A folded vertical antenna has an impedance (and radiation resistance) step-up of four times, but if three quarter-wave wires are used the impedance increases by a factor of nine. This raises the feed impedance to about 300Ω, and the antenna can then be fed with a length of 300Ω ribbon (or via a 4:1 balun to provide a suitable match to 75Ω coaxial cable). This means that the earth system performance becomes less critical. As further advantages, a multi-wire radiating element also lowers the Q and increases the bandwidth of the antenna. This means that its feed line SWR will remain low for a considerable range on either side of its resonant frequency.

When using an antenna of this nature, the three wires must be spaced about 30cm (1ft) apart and, as they use an air dielectric, their lengths can be calculated from the standard formula used to find the length of a quarter-wavelength: 71.32 / f (MHz) metres or 234 / f (MHz) feet.

In many cases it is convenient to use the antenna in a sloping arrangement. Provided that the slope angle does not exceed 30° it will perform almost like a true vertical and provide low-angle radiation. The version shown in **Fig 7.6** is designed for the 3.5MHz amateur band but a half-sized version would be fine for the 7MHz band. Only a 10m (30ft) high single support is needed. It can obviously be scaled for other bands as well. The spreaders S can be fashioned from lightweight 19mm (0.25in) diameter plastic waste pipe.

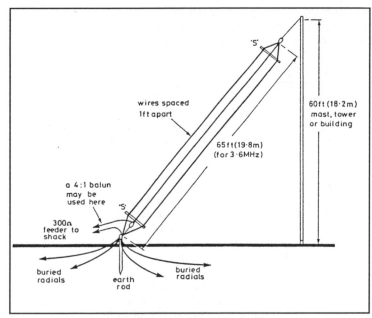

'S'

wires spaced
1ft apart

60ft (18·2m)
mast, tower
or building

65ft (19·8m)
(for 3·6MHz)

a 4:1 balun
may be
used here

'S'

300Ω
feeder to
shack

buried
radials

earth
rod

buried
radials

Fig 7.6 The three-wire sloping quarter-wave vertical has an even greater impedance (and radiation resistance) step-up. This design is for a 3.6MHz version and it has a feed impedance of about 300Ω. A 4:1 balun can be used at the feedpoint and then 75Ω coaxial cable may be run back to the operating position. The increased radiation resistance means that the antenna will work well even with a high-resistance ground system.

Quarter-wave antennas made as folded 'half dipoles' will present similar feed impedances at both their fundamental frequency and at their third harmonic frequency. An antenna of this type, when resonant on 7MHz, will also work on its third harmonic of 21MHz, but will have a different radiation characteristic.

GROUNDED VERTICAL ANTENNAS

Although vertical antennas are normally fed at their base point, it is also possible to adopt a rather novel technique and ground the far end of the antenna, feeding it at the point that would normally be the free end. An inverted-L can be arranged so that its 'elbow' is away from the house and its vertical section comes down to the ground where it is effectively earthed. The horizontal top can be made to run back to the station ATU and its end becomes the feed point of the antenna.

This 'backwards' inverted-L antenna has certain advantages over the more conventional arrangement. There is vertically polarised radiation from the vertical section, and the top of the antenna becomes both a feeder and a loading section. The disadvantage of this technique is that it does bring radiating sections close to the shack or to living areas, but there may be situations where this technique can be used without the dangers of exposure to RF. Constructional details are shown in **Fig 7.7** for situations where it can be arranged that no undue levels of RF will enter inhabited areas.

Although the antenna is designed such that most of the radiation occurs from the vertical section, the horizontal section also radiates. This can be a bonus for it can provide some high-angle radiation for short distance working. An antenna arranged like this can also be put to good use on any of the higher-frequency bands; it will not become neglected or redundant during the summer months when the low bands are often (and mistakenly) ignored. Fig 7.7(a) shows a full-sized quarter-wave vertical antenna having an additional horizontal top feed line which is less than a quarter-wavelength long. Such an arrangement would be best

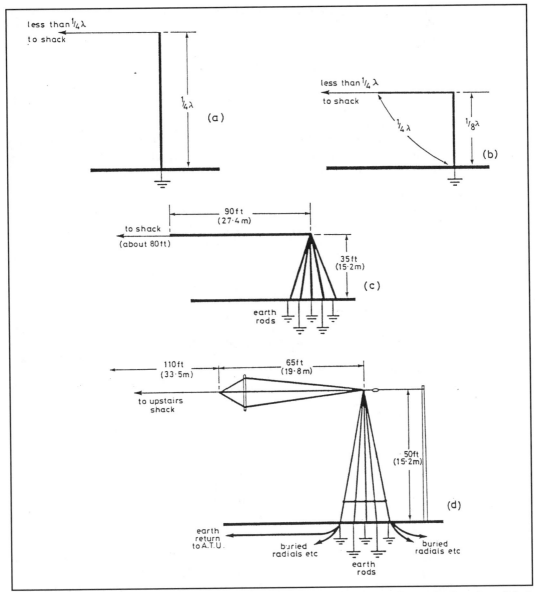

Fig 7.7 (a) A grounded, quarter-wave antenna which is top fed by a single wire. (b) A similar antenna but with only an eighth wavelength in the vertical plane. (c) Here the vertical part of the antenna is little more than 1/16 wavelength but is made with several wires.

adapted for the 7MHz band, for then it would only need to be up to a height of about 10.6m (35ft). At (b) the vertical section is reduced to an eighth-wavelength (which on 1.8MHz is still about 19.2m or 63ft), but the horizontal top is a further eighth-wavelength plus a feeder section which should again be shorter than a quarter-wavelength. By having the feed section under a quarter-wavelength long, the RF current at the feed point will not be high and the radiation there will be reduced.

The scheme shown at (a) has the disadvantage that the vertical section (when used on 7MHz) will be only about 6m or 20ft from the house and will be screened in that direction.

John D Heys, G3BDQ, wrote that he only had a 12m (36ft) mast available when his tests with grounded wires began; the arrangement shown in Fig 7.7(c) was tried. Five wires were brought down to separate earth rods which were arranged in a 2m (6ft) square pattern in an attempt to reduce the earth resistance and also to 'broad band' the antenna by bringing down its inherent Q. The top wire was 51.8m (170ft) long, the first 27.4m (90ft) of which, when measured from the top of the vertical section and added to this, made up a quarter-wavelength on the 1.8MHz band.

The junction of this 27.4m (90ft) length of wire with the remaining 24.4m (80ft) of feed wire is the high-voltage end of the quarter-wave. From this point back to the feed point in the shack the RF voltage falls and the RF current increases to a median value. This means that right at the feed point there will be a medium impedance with some capacitive reactance, which should not present any matching difficulties when using an ATU.

THE 'JUMBO-JAY' VERTICAL

The J-antenna has a long history, which certainly goes back to the mid-'30s, and it is normally used for VHF work (50MHz and up). It is a full-sized half-wave vertical radiator which has at its base a quarter-wave matching section. A half-wave vertical antenna is a vertically polarised and omni-directional free-space radiator which can give excellent low-angle radiation. Its efficiency is 50% which is greater than virtually all quarter-wave vertical ground-plane antennas and it does not need radials or any special earth arrangements.

Centre-feeding a vertical half-wave antenna will mean that its low-impedance feeder would normally come away horizontally from the dipole centre for some considerable distance before dropping to ground. If this is not done, the radiator will be unbalanced and its feed impedance will not remain close to the usual 75Ω. The feed problems are overcome by using a quarter-wave matching section at the foot of the half-wave.

The design of this 'jumbo-jay' antenna is shown in **Fig 7.8**. It is made from wire and the lengths are designed for operation on 29MHz. A non-metallic support (or suspension from a horizontal rope or wire) which is at least 9.1m (30ft) high is needed to hold up the 'J', and a 4.87m (16ft 1in) vertical half-wave length of wire is dropped down from the highest point. The matching

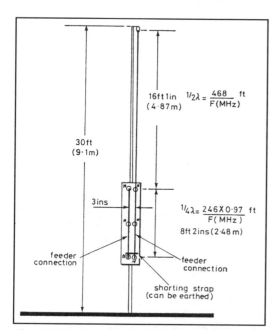

$$\tfrac{1}{2}\lambda = \frac{468}{F(MHz)}\ ft$$

16ft 1in
(4·87m)

30ft
(9·1m)

3ins

$$\tfrac{1}{4}\lambda = \frac{246 \times 0·97}{F(MHz)}\ ft$$

8ft 2ins (2·48 m)

feeder connection

feeder connection

shorting strap
(can be earthed)

Fig 7.8 The 'jumbo-jay' vertical antenna. It is a half-wave radiator which is matched to a low-impedance coaxial feeder by using a quarter-wave stub.

section is arranged to lie along a strip of marine plywood (or similar weatherproof material) so that the base of the 'J' is about 2m (6ft) above the ground. This is low enough to allow an easy adjustment of the matching when setting up the antenna.

The insulation must be good at the top of the antenna and also where the lower end of the radiator joins the matching section. The latter is a non-radiating, end-shorted, quarter-wave length of twin feeder which has a wire spacing of about 75mm (3in). Ceramic or other suitable stand-off insulators can be fixed to the plywood strip to support this matching section.

The 'jumbo-jay' must be tuned to resonance before the 50Ω coaxial feeder is connected. A small shorting bar made with a pair of crocodile clips with a half-turn coil of wire between them can be easily loosely coupled to a dip oscillator. Starting at the lower end of the matching section, the shorting bar should be moved up slowly while continually checking the resonant frequency with the dip oscillator. When the correct setting is found (29MHz), the temporary shorting bar can be replaced with a wire soldered across the matching section and the unwanted remainder cut away.

The coaxial feeder is connected temporarily (by using crocodile clips) across the lower end of the matching section, a few inches above the shorting bar. Then using a low power signal tuned to a frequency near the resonant frequency, check the SWR at various points around this frequency using an SWR meter in the feed line. The tapping points must be adjusted to get the lowest SWR reading and then permanent soldered connections may be made. A perfect match showing an SWR reading of 1:1 may not be attainable but if the reading is 1.5:1 or better the losses will be very small. The centre of the shorting bar can be earthed and this will prevent any build-up of static charge on the antenna.

The 'jumbo-jay' will not have such a wide operating bandwidth as a similar sized antenna constructed with tubing, but it will allow operation over the FM and upper SSB segments of the 28MHz band. It also provides an excellent low angle of radiation that is suitable for both short range FM contacts that generally use line of sight propagation along the earth's surface, and for long haul communications where low angles are needed for the greatest distances.

The commonly found screening factors at some locations caused by buildings, trees and rising ground etc will distort the theoretical all-round radiation pattern of this antenna, particularly as its high-current section is only about 6.7m (22ft) from the ground. When the antenna has been set up and matched it could of course be relocated to a more elevated position and then its performance will be greatly enhanced.

G3XAP 160 METRE ANTENNA

It is no secret that many DX contacts on 160 metres are a result of well-designed antennas and well-planned operating times. However, many people who live in suburban areas do not have the space to erect a large antenna. In fact a horizontal antenna at heights less than a quarter-wavelength from electrical ground radiates little energy at low angles

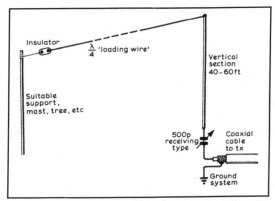

Fig 7.9 The layout and feed system for the 160 metre antenna with a quarter wave loading wire.

and most of the radiation goes straight upwards and is lost into space. This design (**Fig 7.9**), described by A Ashton, G3XAP, in the December 1973 *RadCom* gives an idea for an antenna for 160m that can be accommodated in many suburban locations.

A half-wave dipole can be erected in the so-called inverted-V configuration with the apex considerably less than 130ft high, and produce very good DX results, although anyone with room to erect a full-sized half-wave dipole on 160m is hardly operating from a typical suburban site. The answer is to use a vertical antenna, or one which has its high-current portion vertical to the ground. Even for a vertical it is necessary to load the antenna in some way to bring it into resonance. However, shortening an antenna too much reduces its efficiency considerably, a noticeable difference being seen between a 13m vertical and a 20m vertical at these frequencies.

There are many techniques that can be used for loading. However base loading the antenna means that the current and radiating portion of the antenna is lost in the loading coil. Top loading introduces difficulties in adjustment, and centre loading introduces the need for a centre insulator along with all the attendant mechanical difficulties.

Another option is to take a single wire from the top of the vertical section to a convenient point such as the roof of the house or a tree. This introduces a change in the polar diagram of the vertical, but on 160m the suburban vertical will be anything but omni-directional because of the significant amount of metal that will be within a wavelength or so. The loading wire need not be horizontal - it can slope considerably and can also be bent around the garden - the vertical section is the important part.

The length of the loading wire is chosen to be a quarter-wavelength, making the whole antenna longer than a quarter wavelength. This raises the point of the current maximum to the top of the vertical section and also provides some horizontally polarised signal that is useful for shorter distances. For some people size restrictions may limit the whole length of the antenna to a quarter-wavelength, although this is not felt to be as satisfactory.

The antenna displays an inductive reactance which is removed by simply inserting a variable capacitor at the feed point. Both of the alternatives mentioned so far give rise to feed-point impedances which will almost certainly not provide a perfect match for the feeder, although in both cases the VSWR should be less that 2:1. For improved matching, often required the alternatives shown in **Fig 7.10** may be used, although the coils may introduce some loss.

For the antenna to operate satisfactorily an efficient earth system must be installed. The original antenna was used with an earth consisting of four 45m (140ft radials) which are much bent, sixteen 12m (35ft) radials, and a large number that vary in length from as little as 2m (6ft) up to 10m (30ft).

Using this system and 9 watts input many long distance contacts have been successfully made.

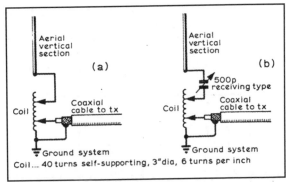

Fig 7.10 Feed systems to provide the minimum level of SWR (a) with a quarter-wave resonant antenna (b) with an antenna greater than a quarter-wavelength.

INVERTED-L FOR MULTIBAND OPERATION

The inverted-L antenna provides a good solution for many radio applications, having a vertical section to provide low angle radiation while the horizontal section also provides some high angle radiation useful for more local contacts. In addition to this the antenna can often be accommodated in a average sized garden, the length being reduced by the vertical section to fit into the plot, while the horizontal section reduces the height of the vertical section of the antenna to ensure that it is not too unsightly.

Inverted-L antennas require a good earth or counterpoise. If metallic objects in or near the house are used, interference with domestic electronic equipment is bound to occur. In addition to this it is always advisable to keep the radiating elements of an antenna away from inhabited areas. This means that it is ideal for the vertical part of the antenna and its ground mat to be located away from the house.

From **Fig 7.11** it can be seen that the system consists of a remote ATU located on the pole carrying the vertical section of the antenna. The wire is carried up the pole and then horizontally towards the house where end loading wires double back using another pole half way back.

The horizontal span of the antenna is only 12m, considerably less than a quarter-wavelength at 3.5MHz. To provide the required loading, traps and inductive loading were considered, but were considered obtrusive, and it could impair the performance on higher frequencies. Capacitive end-loading does not have these disadvantages and two wires were connected to the house-end of the antenna and strung away from the house and towards fence posts on opposite sides of the garden.

To determine the length of the loading wires, the end-loaded horizontal wire should have an

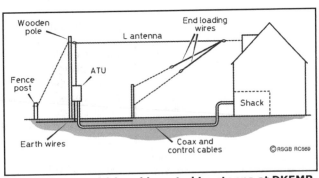

Fig 7.11 The multi-band inverted L antenna at DK5MR.

electrical length of 21m; adding the vertical wire down the 4m pole, the total electrical length, as measured with a dip meter or noise bridge between the down lead and the earth connection, should be 25m. This makes for quarter-wavelength resonance at 3.0MHz and accordingly each end loading wire had to be made 4m long.

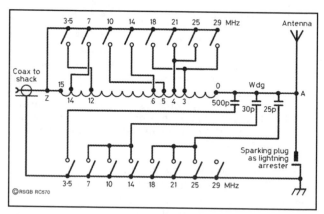

Fig 7.12 The eight band pre-match ATU for the multi-band inverted-L antenna.

The earth system was restricted by the size of the lawn. It consisted of three loops of plastic-covered wire slotted into the lawn. The six ends were run up to an earth bolt in the ATU through a plastic tube (to avoid RF burns to children and pets). This was contained within an area measuring 6 x 8m.

The feed point impedance of the antenna varies widely from band to band. It is lowest at 3.5MHz where it is in the region of hundreds of ohms and highest at 7MHz where it is in the region of thousands of ohms. If this impedance were fed directly by coaxial cable, the impedances seen at the remote end of the feeder would be well beyond the range of the automatic ATU in the transceiver, which is typically 15 - 250Ω.

The solution chosen here is a pre-match ATU on the pole, approximately 2m above ground. It contains an inductor network with coil taps and capacitors for each of the eight bands as shown in **Fig 7.12**. These are selected by relays operated from a control box in the shack. Once adjusted, this ATU transforms the antenna impedance to a value which results in an SWR not exceeding 3:1 throughout each band, so that it should be well within the capability of the automatic ATU in the transceiver. Plots for the levels of SWR that should be seen in the shack are shown in **Fig 7.13**.

The coil, capacitors and relays were mounted on a 215 x 154mm PCB which was housed in a weatherproof plastic cabinet measuring 240 x 160 x 120mm. Another alternative that was tried was to mount the components on a wooden platform and then house the assembly in an inverted ice cream or similar plastic carton. This would need to be firmly secured. All wires enter from below and a drain hole was included for condensed water at the lowest corner.

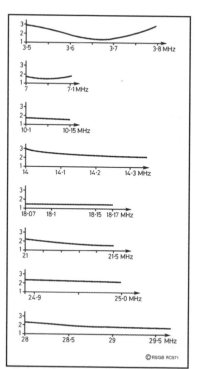

Fig 7.13 SWR vs frequency in the cable between the remote pre-match ATU in the shack.

Two SPST relays were used for each band. They required adequate contact spacing (say 2mm), a current rating of around 5A and insulation. The control box in the shack contains a single pole 8-way switch and an unregulated power supply to match the coil voltage.

The 10-core control cable enters by means of a Centronix-type connector. Of the 10 connections, one operated the two relays for each band, one served as a common earth return, and the tenth was used to key the transmitter in the shack remotely for testing purposes.

The 9µH coil was air-wound with 15 turns of 2mm silvered copper wire wound on a 60mm diameter over a length of 50mm. This can be tapped at each turn.

The capacitors must be rated for high voltage and current operation. At 100W RF at 7MHz, the voltage calculated from the final inductor network values was 575V. The capacitor should be rated at least 1000V. For 3.5MHz a 50V rating is adequate. Small values can be made from open ended lengths of RG58 coax which has a capacitance of 17pF / m. This may be coiled up to save space.

The test equipment was set up close to the ATU. It consisted of the transceiver (adjusted to give its lowest output power, which was then reduced by a 10dB attenuator), a QRP SWR indicator or impedance bridge and coax jumper to the ATU.

A braid strap was soldered to point Z in Fig 7.12 with a miniature alligator clip at the other end; with it, any number of turns of the coil can be shorted out. Similarly, straps with alligator clips were soldered to a foil-dielectric 10 - 500pF tuning capacitor allowing it to be connected between point A and the relay for the band being set up. With the low power used, tuning is easy; everything can be touched with no danger of RF burns.

Starting at 28MHz, the coil tap and capacitor setting for the best SWR was established. The tuning capacitor was then removed and measured - many modern digital multimeters have a picofarad range. A permanent wire from the coil tap just found was then soldered to its relay.

A fixed capacitor, of roughly the value as that which was just measured, but not necessarily of adequate rating, was then soldered in where the tuning capacitor had been unclipped. This must be done because the capacity of this wiring and the open relay will affect the 24MHz band which is set up next. This process was then repeated.

As the search time and price of capacitors adequate for 100W was expected to be considerable, it was found best to complete the whole set-up at low power with junk box capacitors. These can then be replaced with the final versions either obtained specially if not available, or made from RG58/U coax. If it turns out that an exact capacitor value is hard to obtain, the next lower value may be shunted by a small capacitor made of coax or by slightly moving the coil tap.

After all bands work satisfactorily on low power, capacitors with the proper ratings are installed and the SWR is checked again, first at the ATU and

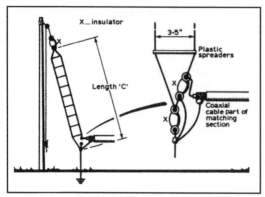

Fig 7.14 Folded unipole antenna.

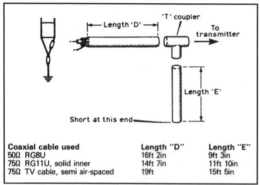

Coaxial cable used	Length "D"	Length "E"
50Ω RG8U	16ft 2in	9ft 3in
75Ω RG11U, solid inner	14ft 7in	11ft 10in
75Ω TV cable, semi air-spaced	19ft	15ft 5in

Fig 7.15 Matching network for the folded unipole antenna.

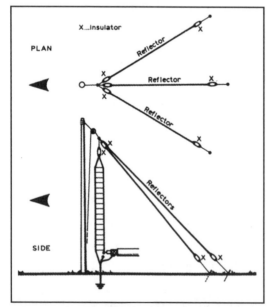

Fig 7.16 The final version of the folded unipole antenna with reflectors.

then at the shack-end of the cable. The SWR in the shack should be the same or a little lower than at the ATU. If all is well, increase power and verify that the automatic ATU can reduce the SWR on all frequencies to where the transceiver will deliver its rated output.

FOLDED UNIPOLE FOR 7 MHZ

An interesting idea for a unipole with considerable gain was described by J Bazley, G3HCT, in the January 1979 issue of *RadCom*. Vertical antennas have a low impedance and can therefore be inefficient. To increases the feed impedance a folded radiator was employed. This consisted of a 10.36m (34ft) vertical radiator constructed from 14SWG (2mm) wire and with 90mm (3.5in) spacing, as shown in **Fig 7.14**.

The feed impedance of a ground fed vertical is around 35Ω, this is multiplied by four in view of the fact that there is a folded radiator. Assuming a typical earth resistance of around 25Ω this gives a total feed impedance of 165Ω. This can be matched using the T-arrangement shown in **Fig 7.15**.

As a further improvement, parasitic reflectors were added to give directivity and gain to the antenna. These were 21.64m (71ft) in length as shown in **Fig 7.16**. This was very successful, although no details were given regarding the change in feed impedance. The antenna was compared with a Yagi at 40m and was only around half to one 'S' point down in strength.

THE MULTEE ANTENNA

This particular antenna is a cross between a vertical and an open wire fed dipole, and it has the convenience of operating on two bands. The dimensions shown in **Fig 7.17** are for a 1.8 / 3.5MHz or a 3.5 / 7MHz combination of bands. Its relatively compact size for the bands involved makes it ideal for many suburban locations.

The antenna operates in two different ways dependent upon the band being used. For the lower frequency band the antenna acts as a vertical with the top section acting as top loading, adding little to the radiation of the antenna. On the lower of the two bands the horizontal section of the antenna radiates. The vertical section acts as a matching stub to transform the high impedance feed point of the doublet to that suitable for the coaxial cable.

For the best operation the vertical section of the T should remain as vertical as possible. In this way omni-directional vertically polarised radiation will be achieved. This is obviously subject to the affects of nearby metallic objects on the radiation of the antenna.

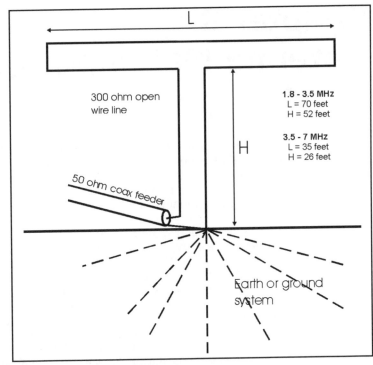

Fig 7.17 The two band Multee antenna.

As the antenna works against ground on the lower frequency band, a particularly efficient earth system is required. Ideas discussed in Chapter 1 may be used. However, for the best results good ground conductivity combined with 20 or more radials and some earth rods would be ideal. For the 1.8 / 3.5MHz version these should be around 20m long, and for the 3.5 / 7MHz version these should be around 10m. Obviously this is only a guide, but a reduction in the earth system will reduce the efficiency of the antenna.

The antenna has been designed for open wire feeder. If the slotted 300Ω ribbon is used account must be taken of the velocity factor. The opaque twin feeder should not be used as this is adversely affected by moisture.

Chapter 8
Antenna Matching Systems

Once an antenna has been designed and installed, it is necessary to ensure that it operates to its maximum efficiency. One key element of this is to ensure that the impedances in the system are matched. In this way the overall antenna system will operate at the optimum efficiency and the best signal is radiated.

To ensure a good match an Antenna Tuning Unit (ATU) is often used. These may also be known as an Antenna System Tuning Unit (ASTU) or Antenna Matching Unit (AMU). These units not only enable a good match to be obtained to ensure the maximum power transfer but they also provide other advantages. In addition to this, semiconductor power devices are susceptible to damage if operated into a poor match. As a result, most modern transceivers reduce the output power if they operate into a mismatched load, often reducing the power significantly when they see a standing wave ratio of 3:1 or more. Worse still, if this protection circuitry is not present, the output devices risk being destroyed. The use of an ATU can prevent this happening.

A further advantage of using an ATU is that - as they consist of a resonant circuit - they may help to limit unwanted or spurious signals from a transmitter, or help to reduce the effect of strong out of band signals to the receiver. They therefore form an essential part of almost any antenna system.

When matching an antenna system there are two areas that need to be addressed: the matching of the antenna to the feeder, and matching the feeder to the transmitter, receiver or transceiver.

ANTENNA TO FEEDER MATCHING

This problem of matching the antenna to the feeder has been discussed at some length in the various descriptions of antennas in earlier chapters, but it is convenient to review some points here as the focus in this chapter is on impedance matching.

In many cases there is little or no problem in matching an antenna to a feeder. When the antenna feed impedance is about 75Ω (as is the case when using a typical half-wave dipole), a coaxial or twin wire feeder having this impedance can be used. If instead a 50Ω impedance coaxial feeder is used with a 75Ω impedance antenna, the additional losses induced by the mismatch are not very great and are quite tolerable. Other antenna systems which have a higher feed impedance can be fed with good quality 300Ω ribbon feeder or an open-wire line that has been specifically made to suit the antenna impedance.

Naturally there are many instances when the antenna impedance does not fall into one of these convenient situations. In particular those which are low and lie between 20 and 50Ω and for which standard coaxial and other cables are not readily available. One way around this matching problem is to use two equal lengths of a standard coaxial cable in parallel. Here two equal lengths of 75Ω coaxial cable may be connected in parallel to provide a 37Ω impedance. This will match into the base of a typical quarter-wave Marconi antenna.

Similarly two pieces of 50Ω coaxial cable provide an impedance of 25Ω. Also, by using two equal lengths of 75Ω and 50Ω cable in parallel, an impedance of 37.5Ω is achieved. However, for this to work they must have the same velocity factor. Even two lengths of 300Ω ribbon feeder can be taped together and, when connected in parallel, they will provide a 150Ω feeder.

Quarter-wave matching transformers can be made easily when the impedances of the antenna, feed line and quarter-wave section do not require particularly complicated arrangements or large combinations of feeders of various impedances. Unfortunately a good match to standard coaxial cables is not always possible when using this scheme, for the characteristic impedance of the transformer may be difficult or almost impossible to devise.

THE HALF-WAVELENGTH LINE

A little-used technique is that of the 'half-wave line' system. This is based upon the fact that the impedance at any point along a wire or feed line is repeated at half-wave intervals, the actual line impedance having no influence upon this characteristic. For instance, if a half-wavelength of 300Ω feeder is connected at one end to the centre of a half-wave dipole (75Ω), it will present a 75Ω impedance at its other end.

The use of half-wave feed lines can be impracticable on the lower-frequency bands unless the antenna is located a long way from the operating position, but there is no reason why any excess feeder (if coaxial cable) cannot be coiled or looped in some way. On the higher frequencies such as 28MHz the half-wave line is rather short (12ft of coaxial cable), and it might only be useful when the antenna is very close to the operating position.

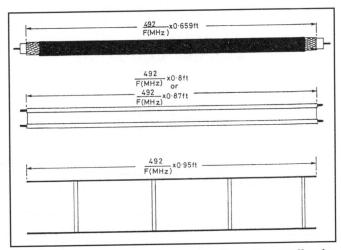

Fig 8.1 How to calculate the length of a half-wave line by multiplying the free-space half-wave length by a line's velocity factor. The older 300Ω ribbon has a velocity factor of 0.8, whereas the slotted variety has a velocity factor of 0.87.

In order to calculate the electrical half-wavelength of a feed line, the free-space half-wavelength of 150 / f (MHz) metres or 492 / f (MHz) feet must be multiplied by the velocity factor of the feeder or cable, as shown in **Fig 8.1**. Most of the commonly used coaxial cables have a velocity factor of 0.66.

When a half-wavelength line is used the antenna feed impedance will be translated to the end of the line where it can be matched to the equipment via a suitable ATU. The losses along such a line will depend upon the characteristics of the coaxial or whatever other type of feeder is used. For most coaxial cables the loss per 30m or 100ft at a frequency of 10MHz is about 0.6dB, rising to around 1.2dB at 30MHz.

Open-wire line and the 300Ω ribbon feeders have much smaller losses than coaxial cable. **Fig 8.2** shows the losses over 300ft of three different types of feeder at 10MHz. It is worth adding that the losses in any coaxial cables increase when their outer insulating sheaths age and are weathered. If any moisture reaches the copper braid, the resulting oxidation increases line losses very considerably.

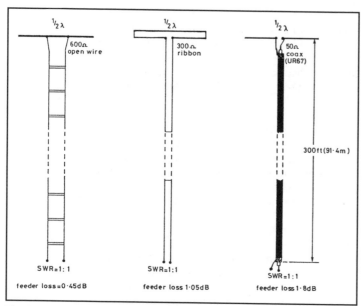

Fig 8.2 Three half-wave dipoles, each fed with a different type of feeder and showing the losses in decibels over 300ft. These losses assume an SWR of unity. The frequency chosen is 10MHz and losses will be greater at higher frequencies.

STANDING WAVE RATIOS

Much nonsense has been written about Standing Wave Ratio (SWR, sometimes called the 'VSWR', voltage standing-wave ratio) measurements on feed lines and it is well worth reminding ourselves that such measurements should be kept in perspective. We hear and read of too many SWR 'horror stories'. Not so long ago, when transmitters had valve output stages, very little attention was paid to the SWR along antenna feed lines. Transmitters, ATUs and antennas were adjusted to get the greatest power levels into the antenna systems, and any impedance mismatches, unless they were particularly large, were ignored. Such mismatches meant that the transmitter output valves were not being fully loaded, and this did not result in the 'sudden death' that can happen to modern solid state output stages in similar circumstances.

To overcome this problem, most commercial equipment now has built-in safety circuits which reduce the power of their output stages when they are presented with a serious mismatch. It is this concern for transceiver output stages which has prompted much of the attention to the correct matching of transceiver outputs to antenna circuits. As a result it makes the proper use of an SWR meter or other indicator almost mandatory.

Fig 8.3 shows a SWR meter connected in the low impedance feed line from an antenna. The SWR meter must be suited to the impedance of the line that is used; this will normally be 50Ω. If a low-pass filter is needed to limit the radiation of transmitter harmonics it must be placed between the SWR meter and the equipment. This arrangement can be unsatisfactory, because few antennas present a perfect match to the feed line used. As a result there is always a mismatch between the feeder and the transmitter. This will either bring about a reduction in power output (for safety reasons) or, if special circuitry is not present, cause output stage overheating. This arrangement also has no additional tuned circuit between the transmitter and the antenna, so it might allow the radiation of spurious emissions from a typical broad-band output stage.

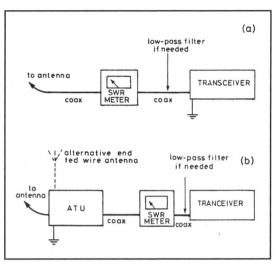

Fig 8.3 (a) An amateur station which has the transceiver connected to the antenna coaxial feed via an SWR meter. (b) This arrangement uses an ATU between the SWR meter and the antenna. A low-pass filter may be needed if the ATU has high-pass characteristics.

Fig 8.3 (b) illustrates a much better way to match the antenna to the transmitter. The ATU is used to match the feeder or the wire antenna impedance to the 50Ω coaxial cable connecting to the equipment (via the SWR meter). When correctly adjusted a near-perfect 50Ω match can be made. The losses introduced by a well-designed ATU are negligible. However, it should be stressed that some poorly designed and built ATUs can introduce a significant loss. Some have been known to introduce losses of 80% or more and there have even been examples of some having such high circulating currents that the soldered connections to their coils actually melted.

An SWR meter measures the forward and the reflected voltage (or current) on the feeder. The ratio of the two readings is the SWR and it is indicated by the meter. If a feeder with a characteristic impedance of 50Ω is connected to an antenna load of either 100Ω or 25Ω, there will be a mismatch and in both these instances the SWR meter will read 2:1. However, the SWR reading does not tell you which of the two possible conditions actually exists. Such a level of mismatch is not really serious unless the losses in the feeder are also large.

There is a multiplication factor of line loss which applies when there is a non-unity SWR on the line. When the SWR becomes 2:1 this factor is 1.25. For example, at 10MHz a 100m or 300ft coaxial line which has an inherent loss of 1.8dB (see Fig 8.1) has a total line loss of 2.25dB when the SWR becomes 2:1. When an SWR is a poor 3.7:1 the total loss on the feeder rises to 3.6dB. In fact a standing wave ratio of 3.7:1 will always result in the doubling of the inherent line loss - a factor worth noting.

Losses of 1dB or thereabouts can be insignificant on their own. A change in level of 1dB is the smallest change that is noticeable by the human ear. Even a 3dB loss (half power) represents little more than a half of an S-point of signal level. It is necessary to keep the level of losses and gains in proportion, seeing the overall picture. However, this should be balanced by the fact that several small gains or losses soon mount up. But it is not worth spending large amounts of money to reduce a loss by 1dB when it is unlikely to have any major impact on the performance of the station as a whole. It is quite likely that these losses could be counteracted by small change elsewhere that might cost far less to implement.

Bearing this in mind, a standing wave ratio of 2:1 will result in a loss of only 1.3dB along 100m (300ft) of 300Ω impedance ribbon used as a 'flat' untuned feeder at 10MHz. The same length of an open-wire feed line has a loss of just 0.56dB when the SWR is 2:1 at the same frequency.

A given SWR reading does not give any indication of the reactive components on the feeder, and it will not be accurate unless the load is a pure resistance. Such reactive components can reach the transceiver output stage, and may cause parasitic oscillations and other problems.

This short discussion on SWR and the examples given may help to reassure those who feel anxious when their SWR meters read 2:1, as this will not cause a noticeable reduction in radiated power on its own. It is only when the levels start to rise above this and the transmitter or transceiver output level is reduced by the protection circuitry that there is a need for concern.

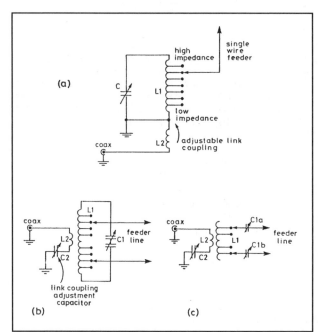

Fig.8.4 (a) The parallel-tuned ATU which will match a fairly wide range of antenna impedances, but presents problems when the impedance is low. The capacitor C must be a high-voltage working type with wide plate spacing. (b) A parallel-tuned circuit ATU that is suitable for use with tuned feeder lines, particularly when they present a high or medium impedance. A fixed link coil L2 can be used and the degree of coupling may be adjusted by C2. (c) This series-tuned ATU uses a pair of ganged (but not electrically connected) variable capacitors in the feed line and it can match low impedances without difficulty. The coupling link is as described for (b).

THE PARALLEL-TUNED CIRCUIT ATU

A parallel tuned circuit can be used as an effective ATU. The circuit is actually similar to that used in the 'tank' circuit of many older valve transmitters. The circuit, although simple as can be seen in **Fig 8.4** at (a), can be used for many end-fed antennas and it can accommodate a wide range of antenna feed impedances.

An ATU should not have a high Q otherwise energy transfer will be difficult to achieve and the tuning will be particularly critical. A Q of between 10 and 12 is ideal, and to achieve a value in this region the tuning capacitor C and the inductance L1 must each have a reactance of about 500Ω at the operating frequency. Even when designed within these parameters a very high antenna impedance might still present matching difficulties. To overcome this the Q may be lowered further by increasing the inductance of L1 and reducing the value of C. A rough rule-of-thumb guide to the correct values of C and L is that the capacitor should be 1pF for each metre of wavelength and the inductor L1 should be 0.25µH for each metre of wavelength of the frequency in use. Calculated values are given in **Table 8.1**.

Band (MHz)	Capacitance value (pF)	Inductance value (µH)
1.8	180	40
3.5	90	22
7	45	12
10	33	8
14	20	6
21	16	4.5
28	11	3

Table 8.1 Table of values of capacitance and inductance for the parallel tuned ATU.

The capability of the tuning capacitor should be accounted when using the circuit with a transmitter. When using a transmitter output power of 100W the tuning capacitor should have a plate spacing of at least 1.5mm (1/16in). Capacitors with smaller spacing than this risk arcing over.

The link coupling coil L2 has one or two turns of wire which can be set at a variable distance from the tuning coil L1. L2 is wound or arranged to be at the 'earthy' end of L1 and the coaxial cable from L2 should reach the transmitter via an SWR meter. Tuning C, trying the different tap positions for the antenna along L1 and also varying the coupling between LI and L2 are three adjustments which must be made to secure the lowest SWR reading. For multi-band work L1 may use plug-in coils which should preferably be self-supporting and wound with heavy wire or thin copper tube. The same link winding may be used on most bands.

AN ATU FOR TWO-WIRE FEEDERS
A variant of the previous design is shown in Fig 8.4 (b), and it is arranged to match a two-wire feed line. In the configuration shown it can accommodate a range of medium to high impedances, and the inductance L1 is tuned by a split-stator variable capacitor. The capacitance across L1 is the effective capacitance of each half of C1 in series. No earth connection to the tuned circuit is shown but the junction of the two sections of the variable capacitor C1 may be earthed. The actual 'earthy' point along the coil will lie somewhere close to its centre and the link winding L2 is arranged over this part of L1.

Fig 8.4 (c) shows another way to match a pair of feeder wires, but in this case it is assumed that the feeder impedance will be low. When this impedance is low a more effective match is made when series tuning is employed, using the two variable capacitors C1a and C1b. Again, no earth connection is required.

Band (MHz)	Value for C2 (pF)
1.8	1800
7	500
10	350
14	220
21	150
28	130

Table 8.2 Table of value for C2 as used in Fig 8.4 (b) and (c).

Both the circuits shown in Fig 8.4 (b) and (c) use link windings L2 which are in series with a variable capacitor C2. This system is much easier to adjust and physically easier to arrange than the variable coupling shown in Fig 8.4 (a).

The component values for L2 and C2 are found from the lowest frequency to be used in the band of intended operation and also the impedance of the coaxial line to the transceiver or transmitter. The capacitor C2 must resonate with L2 on this frequency, ie it will have a value of 1000pF at 3.5MHz when using 50Ω line if the reactance of L2 also equals this impedance. Some approximate capacitance values for six amateur bands are given in **Table 8.2**.

As the capacitances become rather large on the low bands, a larger link winding can be used on 3.5 and 1.8MHz, which means a 500pF broadcast-type variable can be used for C2. This capacitor will also be suitable for the other bands.

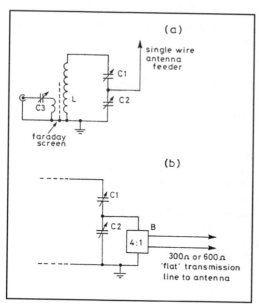

Fig 8.5 (a) A capacitive-tap ATU which can give an infinitely variable impedance match to the tuned circuit L, C1/C2. C1 and C2 are separately tuned and the ratio of their capacitances determines the match. (b) A 4:1 balun may be used to present an unbalanced impedance to the capacitive-tap ATU. This can only be done when the transmission line is of the 'flat' untuned type, such as the feed from a folded dipole when employing a 300Ω ribbon feeder. A balun must never be used with tuned lines.

THE CAPACITIVE-TAP ATU

Instead of using an inductive tap arrangement such as that used in the previous designs, it is also possible to use a capacitive tap arrangement. This has proved to be popular over many years with a variety of operators and today it is still a favourite in many applications. The design is shown in **Fig 8.5** and it is similar to the parallel-tuned circuit but instead of using taps along the coil there are two variable capacitors. These are connected in series and they are used to provide impedance matching and additionally tune the circuit to resonance.

To understand the operation of this ATU, imagine that the antenna wire is at high impedance. It will match when C1 is large and C2 is small in capacitance. On the other hand, if the impedance of the wire is low, C2 will have to be large and C1 will be small. The normal rules of antenna matching Q still apply, so a pair of quite high-value capacitors are needed. Typically values of about 500pF maximum should be suitable for each. As they are always in series and tune across the inductor their plate spacings can be smaller than would be usual when just a single capacitor is employed.

In Fig 8.5(b) either a 300Ω or 600Ω 'flat' and non-resonant feeder line can terminate at a balun (either 1:1 or 4:1 ratio) which will present an unbalanced output to the ATU. A balun must never be used in this position when a tuned line is employed, for the unwanted reactances can give rise to balun heating and there will be a wasteful loss of power. The balun could even be permanently damaged.

L AND PI-SECTION ATUS

L and pi-section ATUs are easy to build and versatile in their operation, forming one of the simplest multi-band ATU designs. The circuit given in **Fig 8.6** at (a) shows the design. Capacitor C1 may be switched in as shown and this makes the circuit into a pi-section ATU, but when it is switched out the circuit it becomes an L-section system. Although the circuit shows a switch associated with C1, it does not actually need to be switched as it can be left in circuit and set to its minimum capacitance.

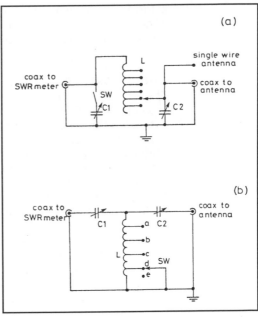

Fig 8.6 (a) An L-section or pi-matching unit. This is a versatile ATU which does not require a coupling coil. A single coil with adequate taps can be used to cover a wide range of frequencies. (b) A T-section ATU which is also a simple matching device. Its greatest disadvantage is that it is poor at rejecting high frequency transmitter harmonics. Its construction is also complicated by the fact that the rotors and stators of C1 and C2 are not at earth potential.

A wide range of impedance loads can be matched to 50Ω with this circuit and either a switched coil or a variable inductor ('roller coaster') may be used for the inductor L. It will be found that if the antenna is at high impedance the capacitance of C1 will be greater than that of C2. A low-impedance input from the antenna requires the converse of this, and then C2 must have the largest capacitance.

In many ways this circuit resembles the previous ATU but the use of a considerable capacitance to ground via either C1 or C2 greatly reduces the chance of harmonic radiation. In effect this ATU also forms a simple low pass filter. It does not need a coupling coil and is also easy to adjust. The disadvantage of this type of ATU circuit is that they cannot match such a wide range of impedances as some of the more sophisticated circuits that have been developed.

The component values for the pi-section ATU which will tune from 3.5 to 28MHz are as follows:

L = 15µH (20 turns of 14SWG, 76mm (3in) diameter and 95mm (3.75in) long. 10 turns are wound at four turns per inch (25mm) and 10 turns are at eight turns per inch. L is tapped every two turns. It may be wound on

a former or air wound. If its diameter is reduced to 50mm (1in), it will need 38 turns of 18SWG at six turns per 50mm (1in).
C1 = 350pF (older-style valve or tube receiver type).
C2 = 200pF (wide-spaced high-voltage type).

T-NETWORK ATU

The T-network design is shown in Fig 8.6 (b) and in this design the inductor L is connected from the live or signal line to ground, effectively in parallel with both the input and the output. Capacitors are in the signal line and must be isolated from earth. This type of ATU is normally only used to match to a low impedance antenna or load. They are ideal when matching quite low values (typically 10 to 50Ω) to standard 50Ω coaxial cables. The voltages across the capacitors C1 and C2 are not high, so wide-spaced transmitting types are not necessary. The inductor L can be tapped for multi band use and again no coupling coil is needed.

Unfortunately this circuit has a drawback: it has a very poor attenuation of transmitter harmonics and behaves as a high-pass filter, with L presenting a high shunt impedance. Nevertheless, it is useful and quite satisfactory when a good low-pass filter is used between the transmitter and the 'T' section.

Component values are not critical, but typical ones for this circuit are:

L = 22 turns of 16SWG enamelled wire 40mm (1.5in) diameter, close wound. The taps down from the top of the coil are:
a = 8 turns (7 - 10MHz)
b = 5 turns (14MHz)
c = 5 turns (18 - 21MHz)
d = 3 turns (24 - 28MHz)
e = no tap (the complete coil is used on 3.5MHz).
C1 and C2 can both be 160pF maximum capacitance broadcast types.

MODIFIED Z-MATCH

The Z-match ATU has been popular for many years, with a number of different versions appearing from time to time. The original Z-match designs were intended for use with valve or tube transmitters. However, for use with solid state transmitters a modified design, developed by the late Louis Varney, G5RV, is more suitable and this is shown in **Fig 8.7**. It can be seen that the 50Ω source is tapped down the main inductors L1 and L2 at T1 and T2. The variable input capacitor C2 is included in Varney's design, and it is a part of

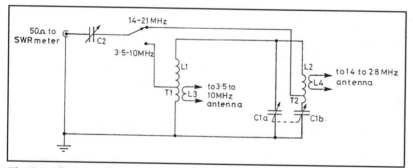

Fig 8.7 The popular Z-match as modified by G5RV. This ATU is well suited to matching both tuned and untuned feed lines, and will cover all the HF bands (3.5 to 30MHz) without band switching.

the series-resonant tuned input circuit which, when correctly tuned, presents a 50Ω non-reactive load to the transmitter.

The Z-match uses the multi-band tuner principle and can cover the 3.5 to 30MHz frequency range without coil changing. The inductance of the high-frequency coil L2 is small enough to be neglected at low frequencies, which means that the two sections of the split-stator tuning capacitor C1a and C1b are then in parallel and tune the inductor L1 over the 3.5 to 10MHz range. At the higher frequencies (14 to 28MHz) L1 is large enough to behave like an RF choke and it has little effect upon the L2 tuned circuit. On these frequencies L2 is tuned by the small variable capacitance provided by C1a and C1b which are in series.

The output coils L3 and L4 are both tightly coupled to L1 and L2 respectively, and are usually arranged to be of a larger diameter than these so they can actually be positioned over them. No output switching is shown in Fig 8.7, but it will be needed in a working model and should connect either L3 or L4 to a twin-wire feeder system. Other switching arrangements, which will allow the connection of unbalanced low-impedance coaxial feeders or instead connect the transmitter output directly to an antenna or dummy load, can be incorporated in the final practical design.

An SWR meter in the line between the transmitter and the Z-match is needed when tuning this ATU. With C1a/C1b set to a median capacitance, the input capacitor C2 must then be adjusted for a minimum SWR reading. C1a/ C1b should then be set to a different value of capacitance and the procedure repeated until the lowest possible SWR is obtained. This process will have to be carried out on each band. A written note indicating the various capacitor settings will allow for rapid adjustment to the correct match on each band as needed.

In use the Z-match does have a rather restricted range of impedance-matching, and it may not always be possible to obtain a really low value of SWR on one or more bands with some antennas. However, the great advantage of the circuit is that there is no need for coil changing or switching even over a wide (often 8:1) frequency range.

Suggested component values for the modified Z-match (as given in *Radio Communication* October 1985) are:

L1	10 turns at 40mm diameter close wound with 14SWG enamelled wire. The tap T1 is four turns from the earthy end.
L2	5 turns 14SWG enamelled wire with the tap T2 made 1.5 turns from the centre of the coil towards C1b.
L3	8 turns 50mm diameter 14SWG enamelled wire over the earthy end of L1.
L4	3 turns 14SWG enamelled wire arranged over the tap T2 on L2.
C1a/C1b	split stator 250 + 250pF variable.
C2	500pF broadcast receiver type.

THE SPC MATCHING CIRCUIT

For a number or years a modified version of the T-match circuit was used by many amateurs. Unfortunately, under some conditions of impedance transformation, the circuit shows a high-pass response and does little to attenuate high-frequency harmonics. To overcome this problem a new circuit, shown in **Fig 8.8** at (a), was devised by W1FB and is known as the W1FB SPC match.

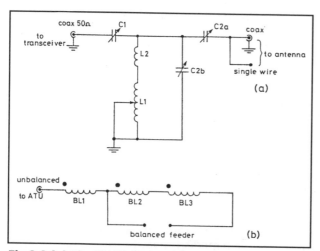

Fig 8.8 (a) The W1FB SPC matching circuit which can match a very wide range of impedances and also provide some considerable harmonic rejection. When using untuned twin wire feeders a balun is required. (b) A circuit for a trifilar air-wound 1:1 balun which is suitable for high-power work. At 100W or less a ferrite core can be used.

The circuit in Fig 8.8 (a) is arranged so there is always some capacitance in parallel with the balanced feeder inductor (L1 + L2). One half of a dual-section variable capacitor (C2b) tunes the inductance and its other section (C2a) is in series and connects the tuned circuit to the output connectors. It is the dual use of this capacitor that gives the name 'SPC' (series-parallel capacitance) to this ATU design.

The harmonic attenuation is good and the bandpass response is maintained when the load impedances range from less than 25Ω to more than 1000Ω. This is because there is always a substantial capacitance in parallel with the inductor L1 + L2 and to earth.

A rotary inductor is frequently used for L1 and the smaller separate coil L2 is used at the high-frequency end of the range of the ATU. This is a self-supporting inductor which must be positioned at right angles to L1. When constructing this design it should be borne in mind that the common and normally 'earthy' spindle between the two capacitor sections of C2a / C2b will not be connected to earth, but to the 'hot' end of the coil. This means that this component should be well insulated from the chassis and have an insulated extension spindle between it and the front panel.

As it is drawn in Fig 8.8, the SPC circuit can load into either a single wire or an unbalanced coaxial feeder. When a 'flat' untuned feeder is used to feed the antenna this may terminate at a suitable (1:1 or 4:1) balun. The unbalanced connection of the balun should be connected to the antenna coaxial cable connection of the ATU.

It is worth mentioning at this point that it is not recommended to use a balun in conjunction with a feeder that has a high level of standing waves. Although in some instances it may work, on other frequencies there will be inevitable high reactances which cannot be tuned out. If the use of a tuned feed line is contemplated it is best matched with a Z-match circuit or one of the circuits shown in Fig 8.4 (b) or (c).

A suitable 1:1 balun for use with the SPC ATU is shown in Fig 8.8(b). This has 12 trifilar turns close wound on a 25mm (1in) diameter former. A ferrite core could saturate with high powers but can be used for power levels below about 100W.

For construction of the SPC ATU, the inductor L1 can be a rotary inductance (25ìH minimum) or a 28 turn coil of 14SWG wire about 65mm diameter (2.5in) wound over a length of 90mm (3.5in). This should be tapped every two turns. L2 consists of three turns of 10SWG wire with a 25mm (1in) coil diameter wound over 40mm (1.5in). This coil is self supporting, and can also be made from 6mm (0.25in) wide copper strip. With an inductance of this specification (L1 + L2) the SPC circuit will tune from 1.8 to 30MHz. For the capacitors, the value of C1 is 200pF and C2 is 200 + 200pF.

It is suggested that the wiring of an SPC matching unit should be made with thin flashing copper strips and that the stators of C2a / C2b are arranged so that they are well above the metal chassis. If this is not done the circuit might not resonate on 28MHz. If a metal cabinet or other enclosure is used it should be big enough to allow adequate spacing between it, the inductors and the variable capacitor stators (about twice the diameter of the coil L1. It is often easier to use a tapped coil rather than a rotary inductor as it provides for much faster band changing. Once the correct tapping points have been found for each waveband, the band switching is simply a matter of changing the position on a switch, whereas using a rotary coil it can be a far more lengthy process.

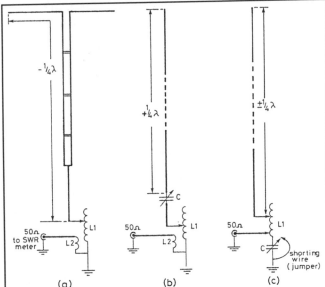

Fig 8.9 (a) Inductive loading a typical G5RV or similar antenna when used as a vertical tuned against ground. The length of half the horizontal top of the antenna plus the length of the 'strapped' feeder should be less than a quarter-wave on 1.8MHz when this tuning method is employed. (b) If the wire to be tuned as a quarter-wave vertical is actually *longer* than a quarter-wavelength, it will exhibit inductive reactance which can then be tuned out with a series capacitor C. The inductor L1 can still be employed as one winding of a transformer and provide coupling to the link winding L2. (c) This combination of L1 and C will allow almost any length of wire to be brought to quarter-wave resonance. The coaxial cable to the equipment is tapped on to L1 at a point which gives a match to its 50Ω impedance.

MATCHING VERTICAL ANTENNAS ON 1.8MHz
The SPC circuit as described will tune down to 1.8MHz but many ATUs cannot be used below 3.5MHz. On 1.8MHz large values of inductance and capacitance are required so it is often advantageous to construct a separate matching unit for this band.

Fig 8.9 shows the typical use of a doublet antenna (often a G5RV type) with its open-wire feeders strapped together and the whole system tuned against ground. The total effective length of this antenna (half the top plus the feeder length) will usually be shorter than a quarter-wave at 1.8MHz, so there will be capacitive reactance at the feed point. This can be tuned out by using a simple series inductance L1. The coil may be of the rotary variable type or instead a fixed inductor which has a number of tap points along its length. L2 is a link winding and uses from three to six turns of insulated wire that is wound over the 'earthy' end of L1.

An RF current indicator in series with the antenna, or an SWR meter in the coaxial cable line to the equipment, can be used to determine the required value of series inductance required.

When an end-fed wire is longer than a quarter-wave it exhibits an inductive reactance. This can be tuned out with a variable capacitor C which is in series with the antenna (see Fig 8.9(b)). However, some series inductance can be used to provide an output coupling transformer L1/L2. The tuning of this arrangement is carried out in the same way as described for the circuit in Fig 8.9(a).

A more flexible ATU is shown in Fig 8.9(c). This can match almost any wire length, and it uses a tapped or variable inductor L1 together with a variable capacitor C between the bottom end of this inductor and earth. A flying lead (jumper) may be connected so that the capacitor C may be shorted out when it is not needed in circuit. Instead of a link winding this circuit has its 50Ω input connected directly over a few turns at the earth end of L1. When the system is made properly resonant by the adjustment of L1 and / or C, the low-impedance feeder can then be tapped on to L1. A near-perfect match is possible if an SWR meter is used in the 50Ω feed line.

Suggested component values for the circuits in Fig 8.9(a), (b) and (c) are:
L1 = 30µH (20 turns 16SWG at 76mm (3in) diameter over 89mm (3.5in) tapped every two or three turns).
L2 = 3 to 6 turns of plastic insulated wire over the 'earthy' end of L1.
C = 250pF variable (broadcast receiver type).

AN 'OUTBOARD' LC CIRCUIT
It is often the case when using a variety of wire antennas for different bands that there is no single matching unit that will give a 100% match on all bands. It can be very frustrating when an ATU which performs perfectly on five or six bands stubbornly refuses to match a particular antenna on just one or two other bands.

A simple end-fed wire can present a wide range of feed impedances if it is used between 1.8 and 30MHz, and one is fortunate if it can be easily tuned and matched to the 50Ω transceiver input / output over this frequency range. If an ATU refuses to match the antenna system one solution is to utilise an 'outboard' LC arrangement as shown in **Fig 8.10** which can compensate for any unusual values of reactance or impedance at the feed point of single-wire antennas.

This circuit has a tapped inductance LR and a variable capacitor CR (with wide spacing), and it can be positioned close to the ATU antenna connection point. No switching is used, and to keep the unit simple and yet flexible three jumper leads with 'crocodile' clips at their ends can be employed to set up a variety of conditions.

As shown in Fig 8.10, a part of the inductance LR is used in series with the antenna and additionally CR is shown shunted to earth across the lead going to the main ATU. Using just CR without any series inductance is possible, or LR alone can be used. Sometimes just a series capacitor is needed and then the jumper lead at A is not connected. B will connect to A and the jumper shown joining to E can be connected to C. The inductor LR can be used in series with the antenna and CR can have one of its connections earthed and its jumper wire at B joined to point A.

This arrangement has been found to work well and can compensate for unusual antenna reactances. It can be connected in a number of different configurations to allow the matching of even the most antennas. Suitable component values can be:

LR = 20µH (22 turns 14SWG at 64mm (2.5in) diameter over 70mm (2.75in) and tapped every two turns).
CR = 200pF with wide plate spacing.

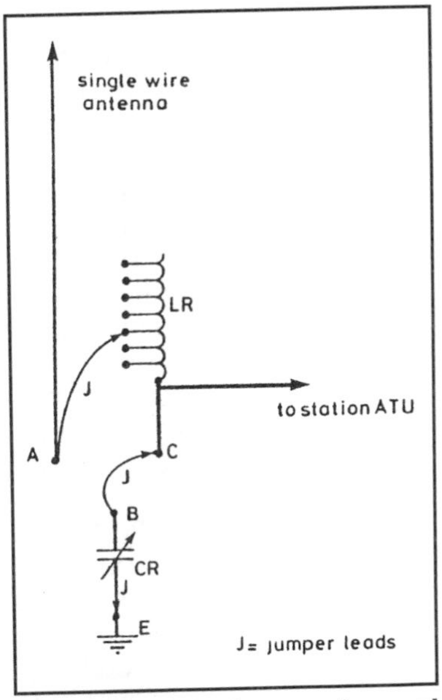

Fig 8.10 This is a universal 'outboard' matching unit which can be used between a single wire antenna and an ATU. This can enable antennas with reactance levels that fall outside the normal tuning range of an the station ATU to be brought within the range that can be matched.

COMMERCIALLY-MADE ATUS

For anyone not wanting to build their own ATU, there is a very good selection of commercially-manufactured items that can be bought through the usual amateur radio stockists. Before an ATU purchase is contemplated, some care must be taken to ensure that it is going to be suitable for the antennas that are presently in use or are likely to be used in the future.

A first consideration must be the power-handling ability of an ATU. Some units are only suitable for QRP and receiving use. Many of those designated for transmitting are only suitable for use with a basic transceiver and can therefore safely operate with transmitter output powers of about 150W at the most. If a linear amplifier is to be used the ATU must be rated to somewhere between 500W and 2kW peak power; the variable capacitor plate spacing seems to be the most important factor. It is the high voltage rating of the components used which make such ATUs expensive.

Another most important feature, which is not often explained satisfactorily in advertisements, is the ability of a commercial ATU to match a very wide range of impedances. Many of these units can only match a limited impedance range and are really only suitable for low impedance input work. They have a working impedance of between 25 and 100Ω and are certainly not suitable for end-fed wire antennas which may present an impedance of 1000Ω or more on some bands.

A good ATU (such as one based upon the SPC circuit) will match a very wide impedance range but many of the small matching units that have been designed to be used with particular 'black boxes' will only match antenna impedances (or feeder impedances) up to a maximum of 500Ω.

Most of the commercial ATUs now include several switching options which allow a variety of coaxial inputs, end-fed wires or even 'flat' untuned twin lines (using a balun) to be matched. They often also have a switched connection to an external dummy load and some have integral SWR meters. The more expensive models also have power output meters and they can be switched to several power level ranges. These ATUs may be able to measure output powers from under 1W up to 2kW or even more. Auto-tune ATUs are becoming more popular but many of these have a limited impedance-matching range.

ATU POTPOURRI

Whatever type of ATU is used, its chassis must be the common earth point for the station, with all the equipment connecting to its earth terminal.

When building an ATU it is necessary to ensure that there is sufficient space within the case that is used. Many home built units are squashed into metal boxes that are much too small, with the coils almost touching the cabinet tops or sides. The wire used must also be thick enough. It is worth remembering that the skin effect applies and the RF signals will only be conducted towards the surface of the wire. Accordingly the real resistance seen by the RF is higher than that measured by a DC ohmmeter, and as a result some power may be dissipated as heat in the ATU and not radiated. Accordingly a wire thickness of 14SWG or thicker should be used when winding ATU coils.

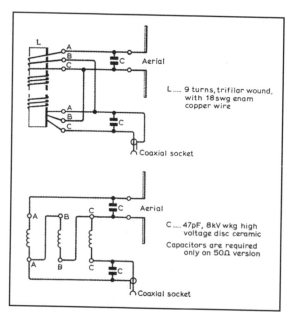

L..... 9 turns, trifilar wound, with 18swg enam copper wire

C ..... 47pF, 8kV wkg high voltage disc ceramic

Capacitors are required only on 50Ω version

Fig 8.11 Winding details for the G3PTN balun.

In some cases what is termed 'flash over' may be experienced on the ATU variable capacitors, especially on SSB speech peaks. This is either because the plate spacing of these capacitors is too small or the Q of the tuned circuit is too high. A high-Q circuit will not allow the proper transfer of power to the antenna, so there are high RF voltages built up which cause the 'flash over'.

Any sign of coil heating is a warning that the LC ratio or Q is incorrect. A good and efficient ATU never has coil heating, for its throughput of energy is high. A loss of 3dB within an ATU means that half the transmitter power is contributing to heating and other losses.

Baluns

Baluns are a component that should be used whenever making a transition between balanced and unbalanced systems. For example they should be used when feeding a dipole with coaxial feeder. The cost of commercially made items is one issue that deters many people from including them as part of the antenna. While it is possible for the antenna to operate satisfactorily for many purposes without one, their use is to be advised. They provide a number of advantages, including ensuring that RF is not radiated or received on the feeder and in this way they may reduce the possibility of interference with nearby radio and televisions.

Baluns are quite easy to build and a number of ideas have appeared in the magazines over the years. One by Zygmunt Chowaniec, G3PTN, that appeared in the November 1974 issue of *RadCom* described a design for using the ferrite from a discarded medium wave radio. It uses trifilar windings on one of these ferrite cores using 18SWG enamelled copper wire, see **Fig 8.11**. For powers up to 1kW SSB G3PTN states that a core of 12 to 15mm (1/2 to 5/8-in) is adequate. Two or three 6mm (1/4-inch) cores can be taped together using PVC tape. The lengths of the rods are not critical and with 18SWG 50mm or 2in is sufficient. Before winding the core should be covered with a single layer of tape. Nine turns are needed and three 50cm (20in) lengths of wire are required. The windings should be as tight and as close as possible.

The balun transformer can be mounted in a metal container. The way in which this was achieved by G3PTN using a container obtained from a chemist is shown in **Fig 8.12**. It was then potted using epoxy resin, or it could just be waterproofed.

If the balun is to be used with a 50Ω cable the capacitors labelled C in Fig 8.11 should be fitted as these tune out the reactive component at higher frequencies. They reduce the loss to almost zero at 28MHz.

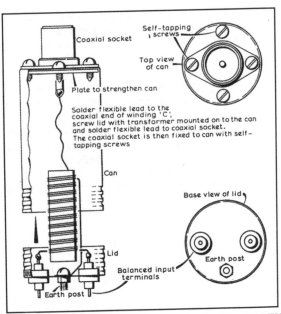

Fig 8.12 Mounting arrangements for the G3PTN balun.

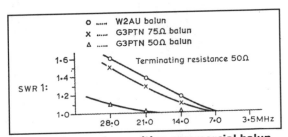

Fig 8.13 Comparison with a commercial balun.

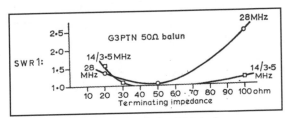

Fig 8.14 Performance of the 50Ω balun.

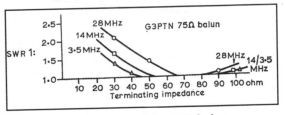

Fig 8.15 Performance of the 75Ω balun.

The performance of the balun was investigated and a comparison undertaken against a commercial item. The results are shown in **Fig 8.13** and the overall performance of the individual baluns is shown in **Figs 8.14** and **8.15**.

Another interesting idea for a balun appeared in 'Technical Topics' (*RadCom*, August 1988) from information that appeared in *Radio-ZS* March 1988 based on information in *QST* October 1980. It is shown in **Fig 8.16** and describes an effective home-made dipole centre and air-cored balun based on a commercially made item rated at 4kW peak and exhibiting a loss of only 0.5dB.

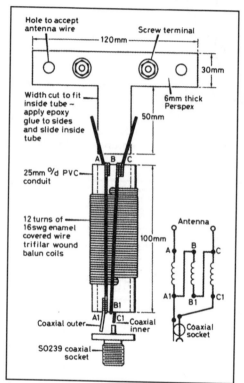

Fig 8.16 The exploded view of the ZS2LR dipole centre with integral 1:1 air cored balun.

The reason for using an air cored former is that when baluns are overloaded or subject to a high level of standing waves harmonics and intermodulation products are generated. Air spaced baluns are not subject to saturation, ringing or harmonic generation and in this way they may be preferred in some situations.

The balun covering 3 - 30MHz comprises 12 turns of 16SWG (1.6mm) wire, trifilar wound on a 25mm (1in) former. For a lower frequency version covering 1.8 - 7MHz, use 13 turns on a 50mm (2in) former. The balun constructed by ZS2LR combined the balun with a dipole centre insulator. The insulator was made of laminated Perspex cut to a T-shape with the vertical portion of the correct dimension to fit inside a piece of 25mm PVC conduit. In the diagram connecting wires appear on the outside of the coil. The diagram has been drawn in this way for clarity, but normally these would be routed on the inside of the coil. Terminals were provided on the insulator for the connection of the antenna and balun wires.

An SO239 connector was mounted and connected at the bottom of the former. The overall construction was undertaken by first winding the coil, making the balun connections and then securing the balun former to the T insulator. Finally the socket was connected and the balun connected to the insulator terminals. The balun was then wrapped with cotton gauze bandage to cover the windings and filling all gaps that might allow water ingress. As well as securing the connector to the balun former. The cotton gauze was then impregnated with epoxy glue and allowed to cure. The antenna was then attached to the terminals, the feed line plugged in and the socket sprayed with Tectyl to prevent ingress of moisture and corrosion.

Chapter 9
Practical Aspects

The practical aspects of installing antennas are just as important in many respects as the electrical ones. There used to be sayings that if an antenna did not fall down occasionally then it was not high enough. While this may appear amusing, an antenna is no use when it is on the ground, and of course it will fall just as a contest is about to start or there is another reason for wanting to use the system. There are also safety issues to consider. Falling antennas can cause damage and injury, and although injury or damage is less likely in the case of wire antennas, it is still a possibility that needs to be taken seriously.

Installing an antenna in the correct fashion can extend its life as well as ensuring that it operates correctly. In summary, the installation can often add as much to the antenna as the design and location.

SAFETY
One of the first things to emphasise when installing an antenna is that of safety. Although amateur radio is generally a very safe hobby to enjoy, accidents can happen and some have occurred in the past. There have been injuries, and even fatalities of people installing antenna systems. Fortunately these occurrences are few and far between. To prevent any accidents from occurring it is always necessary to think of the safety aspects of antennas and their installation. Do not take risks, especially as they may involve other people. Not only consider the actual installation, but also the long term life of the antenna itself. If it falls, will it fall in a dangerous fashion, and is it likely to cause injury?

While it is impossible to set down hard and fast rules, a summary of some guidelines from the *ARRL Handbook* was included in the *HF Antenna Collection* and this gives a good outline to follow.

No antenna project is worth doing if it cannot be done in complete safety. It is largely a matter of your wits against Murphy's Law, which says that "anything that can go wrong will". The following safety rules may seem obvious but plan before you begin.

Start by asking yourself, when designing your system:

- What risks would the antenna present while it is up?
- Could anyone touch a 'hot' part of it and get and RF bum?
- Could visiting or trespassing children climb a tower and get hurt?
- Could pranksters or vandals easily undo or cut a guy wire?
- Have you thought of lightning?
- What would be the consequences if any part of the installation fails in foul weather or due to corrosion?

Belt-and-braces are mandatory if there is any risk of any displaced part of the installation touching an overhead power line; a similar approach may be wise with regard to your neighbour's greenhouse!

For less dangerous spots, consider this technique: make that part of the installation capable of doing most damage because of its weight or location as solid as you can. Most often this will be the mast or tower, or at least its lower part; power or telephone line construction shows how this is done. All other parts of your installation such as mast tops, antennas proper etc, are then constructed much lighter and if something is going to give one of them will and without wreaking much havoc on the way down.

How are you going to get your creation up there? More accidents happen during antenna erection or removal than at any other time. Again, be particularly wary of power lines.

List in sequence each step, from initial assembly to final adjustment, and for each step the parts, hardware, tools and instruments required. This will not only avoid interruptions for avoidable trips back to the shack or shop but will help keep you from running out of daylight and your helpers from running out of patience. Needless to say, working in the half-dark or with too few hands adds unnecessary hazards.

Some of the best designs can be safely put up by two people but extra help does make it easier. Do you have liability insurance, just in case? If you must climb to get your antenna up, observe these rules:

Do:
- Wear suitable clothing: long sleeved pull-over shirt, long trousers without cuffs, shoes with no-slip soles and well-defined heels, gloves.
- Use a safety belt wherever possible.
- Check your safety belt, ropes, pulleys before each use.
- Tie your tools, gloves, with string so they will not fall far if you drop them.
- Wear a hard hat when ground-crewing for a climber.

Don't:
- Climb a wet tower, roof, ladder.
- Remain aloft when tired or cold.
- Climb an extended crank-up tower.
- Leave a tilt-over tower unlocked when upright.
- Play the clown when climbing.

These ideas give a general outline of some of the measures that can be taken. If safety is kept in mind at all times, it will make sure that accidents do not happen and ensure that amateur radio remains the very enjoyable hobby that it is.

RIGGING

One major element of the installation is the use of guys, ropes and rigging. A very useful article was published in *RadCom* in March 1970 written by

J Michael Gale, G3JMG. Antennas have to withstand the rigours of the elements and must be constructed with great care and expertise if they are to offer any degree of reliability. Knowing the right knot, and how to tie it, is just as much a part of the complete radio amateur as the ability to make a sound soldered joint. Rigging masts and wire antennas is a direct application of elementary seamanship and many of the same principles applied to ship rigging can be applied to antenna poles, masts and ropes.

ROPE

Rope comes in a wide variety of sizes, materials and forms of construction (known as 'lay'). The most popular form is the traditional three-strand variety with the 'right-hand thread'. It is given a right-hand twist because most people are right-handed and it is their natural tendency to coil the rope in a clockwise direction.

Before discussing the multiplicity of materials let us be quite clear about its size. In Britain, rope was traditionally measured by its circumference in inches. This confuses most engineers, who are more used to considering something of round section by its diameter. Very roughly, the diameter of rope is about one third its circumference. So a ¾-inch rope is about ¼-inch in diameter. With metrication, however, this has changed and rope is measured by its diameter in millimetres and what was a ¾-inch rope is now a 6mm rope, although there may be some references in older literature to the old nomenclature.

Until comparatively recently all rope was made of one of several vegetable fibres such as hemp, manila, cotton, sisal etc. Although these fibres have different characteristics, they all have one failing in common - they absorb water, swelling in both length and diameter in the process, and they are attacked by bacteria and rot. For this reason rope was never very popular for use as permanent mast guys as it required continual adjustment and frequent replacement. Guys were therefore invariably made of galvanised wire, although this, too, eventually corroded, and they also have to be split up into short lengths by insulators to reduce the absorption of RF.

Modern ropes made from synthetic fibres offer a tremendous advance in that they do not swell when wet; they resist petrol, oil, acids and alkalis well, and, above all, do not rot. Also, synthetic ropes are generally much stronger than natural fibre ropes and are, therefore, ideally suited for use as guys.

The basic principles of rope making have not altered for hundreds of years. Threads of the fibre are first twisted into yards which are then laid together in a spiral twist to form the strand, and finally, the strands (usually three) are laid around each other to complete the rope. This method puts an even load on all parts since all the threads run more or less straight along the direction of the load. Look at a rope and see.

With synthetic fibres, however, there is one important difference. Natural fibres, which make up the basic yam, occur only in short lengths called 'staple' fibre. It is the loose ends of these fibres sticking out of the side of the rope which gives it the familiar hairy finish. Synthetic fibre, however, comes in a continuous filament - each one as long as the rope itself. This contributes to the greater strength of synthetic rope and also gives it a much smoother, shinier finish. This can make the rope slippery and difficult to grip, so sometimes the continuous filament is cut into short lengths to resemble staple fibre, thereby giving it the traditional 'hairy' finish. It does weaken it a little, however. The continuous filament also allows the yarns to be plaited or braided. This makes for a kink-free rope (very popular with water-skiers) but it is not as strong as the conventional three-strand construction and it is much harder to splice.

One undesirable feature common to all synthetic rope is the fact that it melts. This is of little significance for most general purposes but it has to be watched very carefully by a seaman when easing a rope round bitts or cleats. This feature can be turned to advantage, however, as it obviates the necessity of whipping the ends to prevent fraying - while this is still the best way, a quicker method is to fuse the end in a clean flame then round off with wet fingers to prevent it sticking. This is best done before cutting; rotate a 1in section of rope in a clean flame until fused all round, then cut through with a sharp knife when cool. The two jobs can be done in one by using a hot soldering iron (the professionals use an electrically-heated knife blade).

Just as the various natural fibres have differing characteristics, so do the various synthetic fibres and, to enjoy the full benefits, it is vital to understand their differences.

Nylon

This is a polyamide filament derived from coal and oil; it was one of the first synthetic rope fibres and is still the strongest. For example, a dry nylon rope of 1in circumference (8mm diameter) and of conventional three-strand construction (hawser-laid), will break at about 1.3 tons. White in colour, it tends to be rather hard to handle unless plaited or braided. It absorbs a little moisture and loses about 10% of its strength when saturated. It resists strong alkalis well but is expensive.

Nylon's most important characteristic is its fantastic elasticity, enabling it to stretch up to 20% before breaking. This makes it ideal for use in situations where high shock loads would normally break a wire - such as in towing, for example. By the same token, however, this feature makes nylon most unsuitable for supporting a mast; the guys could be tuned like guitar strings but the mast would still wave about like a Caribbean palm. However, nylon would be suitable for use as an antenna halyard; the elasticity would keep the wire taut under all conditions of wind and temperature, but there are cheaper ways of obtaining this desirable effect. Do not make the common error of referring to all synthetic rope as 'nylon'. If you ask for nylon in a ship chandler's, nylon is what you will get but it may be useless for your purpose.

Terylene

This is polyester filament derived from oil. It is very similar in appearance to nylon but not quite as strong; the same 1in three-strand rope breaks at about one ton, but this strength is maintained when wet. In some respects Terylene is the converse of nylon in that it resists acids well and stretches very little under load. The small amount of stretch can be reduced still further by a pre-stretching process during manufacture, making Terylene a virtual non-corrosive substitute for wire with the added advantage of also being non-conductive. Pre-stretched Terylene is, therefore, the ideal rope to use for mast guys and halyards, but it is also, unfortunately, the most expensive.

Terylene is the trade name of ICI. The same material is made in the USA, where it is called 'Dacron' by Du Pont, and by Hoechst Chemicals in Germany, where it is called 'Trevira'. To avoid confusion, many rope manufacturers now describe the material as polyester.

Polythene

Also derived from oil, this was the first cheap general purpose synthetic rope fibre and is often referred to as 'Courlene', which is the trade name of the basic fibre. In its early days it was always coloured bright orange but it is now available in a variety of colours, including black and white. The fibre, and therefore the rope, is hard, and wiry and very smooth; the surface always feels greasy so this rope is easily recognised. It is about 50% stronger than natural fibre ropes but not as strong as nylon or Terylene; the 1in size breaks at about 1500lb. Under load the stretch is a little less than nylon but much greater than Terylene. It is very light in weight and floats.

When it was first introduced, polythene rope became very popular for general use on account of its low cost, the price being less than half that of Terylene. There are snags, however, the main one being the extreme difficulty in making knots and splices hold securely due to its springy and 'greasy' nature. It is still, surprisingly, popular for use in the manufacture of fishing nets, but for general purposes its popularity rapidly declined with the introduction of polypropylene.

Polypropylene

This is another oil-derived polyester fibre and the latest introduction into the rope field. It is the currently most popular all-round general purpose rope on account of its excellent compromise with regard to performance and price. It has 90% of the strength of Terylene (the 1in size breaking at about 2000lb), yet is only half the price. Under load it stretches slightly more than Terylene but nothing like as much as nylon or polythene. It combines the acid-resistance of Terylene with the alkali-resistance of nylon. The fibre is a little harder than Terylene or nylon but not as hard or so 'greasy' as polythene. It is light and floats.

When first introduced it was invariably sold under the fibre's trade name of 'Ulstron' and coloured green, but it is now available in a wide variety of forms and colours. The basic fibre is commonly a continuous round section filament about the thickness of a human hair called 'monofilament' when made up into rope. It can also be supplied as an extremely fine strand which is then called 'multifilament' in rope form. This form is much softer and more flexible than monofilament but is more expensive because of the extra work involved in manufacture. The fibre may also be rectangular in section; this is obtained by splitting a flat sheet or film of the material which is then called 'fibrefilm'. This results in a coarse rope which tends to be rather rough on the hands but it holds knots and splices much better than any other continuous-filament rope. In addition, the monofilament fibre can be cut into short lengths to produce a staple fibre rope of the traditional hairy appearance. Thus, this one basic material can be used to produce four very different types of rope, all with a similar strength.

These, then, are the current most popular rope-making materials. For amateur radio use, pre-stretched Terylene / Dacron / Trevira makes ideal guys and halyards but is expensive. As this material suffers less from ultra-violet degradation than most other fibres, its use is especially recommended in those parts of the world which enjoy more than their fair share of sunshine. Nylon is unsuitable for guys but could be used for halyards, although this, too, is expensive. In the UK, northern Europe and other places which would welcome some more sunshine, monofilament polypropylene, although quite a mouthful, is an excellent general-purpose rope equally suitable for use as guys or halyards which will give years of reliable service at little cost.

THIMBLES
Whenever the end of the rope is formed into a loop to transfer strain to a metal fitting such as a hook, eye-bolt or pulley, it must be protected by a thimble to spread the load correctly and prevent chafe. This is especially important with polypropylene, which seems to be particularly susceptible to chafe. Thimbles are commonly pear-shaped troughs of suitable size to take a particular size of rope but they can also be circular for special purposes. They may be made of galvanised steel, stainless steel or nylon. The stainless ones are extremely strong and expensive and are usually reserved for use with stainless steel wire. The traditional galvanised ones are 'cheap and cheerful', the finish tends to be rough, which partly defeats their object, and they eventually corrode anyway. They can also set up a highly corrosive electrolytic action if used in contact with a dissimilar metal at sea or in coastal areas. For synthetic ropes nylon thimbles are preferred; they cost very little more than the galvanised ones but cannot corrode, cause electrolytic action or damage the fibres.

Thimbles are measured by their overall length, but the 'score', or the width across the trough, is also taken into consideration as this must suit the size of rope it is to take. When a thimble is spliced into the end of a rope it is known as a 'hard eye'; without a thimble the spliced loop (eye-splice) is called a 'soft-eye'.

SHACKLES
These are commonly D-shaped devices (although there are other shapes for special purposes) to link hard eyes, pulleys, eye-bolts, pickets etc. They may be made of galvanised steel, stainless steel, manganese bronze or even nylon. Like chain, they are measured by the diameter of the bar from which they are formed and can range from ½-inch to 2in or more. In the smaller sizes the diameter of the screwed pin which forms the stroke of the D is usually the same as the rounded part but, in the larger sizes, the pin is often one size larger.

Stainless steel shackles are very strong and last forever but are expensive. The galvanised ones are strong and cheap but eventually rust where the plating is worn through at the points of contact, and the threaded parts, which cannot be galvanised, quickly seize with rust unless treated with thick grease - preferably anhydrous lanolin - at frequent intervals. Shackles made of manganese bronze are not as strong as those of steel but have the advantages that they cost only a little more than the galvanised ones and do not corrode. Nylon shackles are usually reserved for use with nylon chain which finds such light-duty applications as mooring marker buoys or marking out exhibition stands etc. The choice usually lies between galvanised or bronze.

The unthreaded end of the pin is flattened and has a small hole through it. It is tightened by slipping it into the tapered slot in a special key or in the side cheek of a seaman's knife - not, please not, with pliers. Alternatively, the pin may be tightened by passing a thin, hard steel bar, such as a small Allen key, through the hole, but the main purpose of the hole is to enable the pin to be 'moused', that is locked, by twisting wire through the hole and round the bar. For long-term use, especially at sea or in coastal areas, the wire should be of similar material to the shackle to avoid electrolytic action, ie copper wire with bronze shackles and galvanised wire with galvanised shackles. Marine grade stainless steel (EN 58 J) does not cause electrolytic action, so wire of this material may safely be used with any shackle or rigging screw and any non-corrosive wire such as copper may be used with stainless shackles.

PULLEYS

For reliable service in any weather conditions, only genuine marine fittings should be used. They cost somewhat more than cheap washing-line pulleys but are a much better investment as they do not corrode, jam or seize, and require no lubrication or maintenance. Modern marine pulley blocks may be made with synthetic resin bonded fibre cheeks and sheaves and chromium-plated manganese bronze bearding and straps, or with stainless steel cheeks and nylon sheaves. The stainless type costs fractionally more than the other type but there is little to choose between the two in terms of strength and reliability. There is a minimum diameter of sheave for every size of rope and there may be up to three sheaves in one block.

For a simple halyard pulley, a straightforward single sheaved block will suffice but to make up a tackle for raising a mast one of the pair of blocks must be provided with a 'becket'. This is simply a point of attachment below the block for securing the fixed end of the rope. The apparent power gain varies directly as the number of ropes at the moving block. Thus, two single-sheaved blocks, one with becket, will give a 2:1 advantage in one direction and 3:1 in the other. A single and double gives 3:1 or 4:1, and a pair of doubles gives a 4:1 or 5:1 advantage according to the direction of pull. The term 'apparent power gain' is used because power is a function of time and although a lifting tackle may be rigged to give a 4:1 advantage, it will take four times as long (and five times as much rope) to do the job. In fact about 25% of the advantage will be lost through friction in the sheaves.

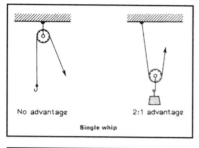

No advantage   2:1 advantage

Single whip

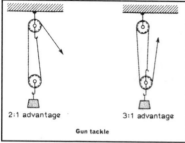

2:1 advantage   3:1 advantage

Gun tackle

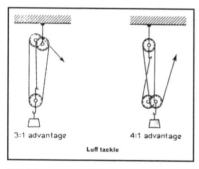

3:1 advantage   4:1 advantage

Luff tackle

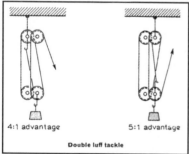

4:1 advantage   5:1 advantage

Double luff tackle

Fig 9.1 Pulley arrangements.

The various arrangements are shown in **Fig 9.1**, (a) and (b).

ANTENNA WIRE

Have you ever wondered how telephone land-lines remain intact year after year although antennas frequently collapse? One of their secrets is in the wire which is made to their own special recipe. The addition of one per cent cadmium to the basic copper increases the tensile strength of hard-drawn wire by 50% from 20 tons psi (per square inch) to 30 tons psi: it also increases the DC resistance by nearly 25% but do not let this worry you too much, the vital thing is to keep some wire up in the air: a highly conductive pure copper antenna is quite useless laid on the ground. In the days of airborne HF communications, the RAF used quite thin stranded stainless steel antenna wire, and modern yacht installations invariably utilise part of the galvanised or stainless steel rigging for the antenna. And remember, stainless steel has DC resistance nearly 53 times that of copper.

Telephone wire is rather quaintly measured by its weight per mile; standard sizes being 40lb, 70lb and 100lb, which approximate to 18, 16 and 14SWG, respectively. Either the 70lb or 100lb sizes make good antennas. An antenna farm of HF rhombics and dipoles constructed entirely of 70lb telephone wire has been in successful operation for many years at the University of Sheffield's Radioastronomy Research Station which is 1350ft up in the Yorkshire Pennines. The same Department of Physics also used this wire at their research station with the British Antarctic Survey, so do not blame British weather for your antenna's demise. British Standard Specification 175/1951 reveals all about telephone wire.

Another secret, which goes hand-in-hand with the wire, is the method of joining and fastening it. A copper tube 3.5in long and of oval section, just large enough to take the two wires side-by-side, is placed in a simple hand tool which clamps the ends while the centre section is rotated through 360. This cold-welds the wires quickly and easily, making a perfect electrical and mechanical joint without annealing the wire.

If plain copper wire is used it should be of the hard-drawn variety; common sizes being 14SWG or 7 / 0.029. Hard-drawn wire is usually left bare, although it can be covered; it cannot be enamelled as the drying process anneals it.

Joints and fastenings

With wire antennas, solder should never be used to make a mechanical joint. The necessary heat anneals the section of wire, making it soft, and the solder stiffens the joint so that tensions and movement quickly fracture the wire at the joint. Unless telephone wire and the special 'sleeve jointing' are used, there is little one can do with solid wire except to form a loop through the eye of the insulator or round a thimble and wind the short end round the standing part. It is easier on the fingers if the short end is first passed through a small hole near the end of a short piece of wood which can then be turned like a key. Do not try tying knots in wire.

With standard wire British Telecommunications (BT) use an excellent, but simple, splice. The loop is formed and the short end laid alongside the standing part. Then one strand of the short end is untwisted back to the loop and wound tightly round both parts. Another strand is treaded likewise and so on until the one remaining strand is wound round the standing part alone. This results in a beautifully tapered splice of great strength. The BT standard is a minimum of two and a half turns of each strand and it is recommended that at least four turns be made. Have a look at the stay on a telegraph pole.

If the stranded wire is insulated and there is some reluctance towards stripping the covering, the two parts can be bound together by a flat seizing using waxed or tarred whipping twine. Do not use Terylene whipping twine; it is extremely strong but it slips. If the proper waxed twine cannot be obtained, ordinary thin string can be used provided it is made waterproof afterwards by melting in beeswax or even candle wax with a warm soldering iron. This method is ideal at the elbow of an inverted-L to avoid cutting and rejoining the wire. The temptation to use bulldog grips should be avoided at all costs. Not only are they extremely ugly, they cripple copper wire and reduce its strength enormously.

For a temporary job, rope can be tied to an insulator with a bowline. This is an excellent knot for making a loop, being one of the few knots guaranteed not to slip under any circumstances, and it is readily untied. However, it is not generally appreciated that all knots greatly reduce the strength of the rope and should be regarded as temporary fastenings only. In the case of the bowline the strength is reduced to about 65%. For a permanent job an eye splice (**Fig 9.2**) is far superior, retaining 90 to 95% of the rope's strength, and it is much neater too. Besides, it is the mark of the expert and impresses visitors enormously. Do not betray the secret that splicing is one of the few things which turns out to be much easier than it looks. All the relevant knots, splices and seizings that may be used for antenna systems can be learned in an hour. Because of the smoother nature of synthetic rope, splices must be given a minimum of five tucks.

(a) Break open the fused end of the rope, making sure that the individual fibres of the three separate strands remain firmly fused. With 3 or 4in of rope; form a loop in the shape of a 'D' with the unlayed end on the right. Arrange the three strands so that two of them go off to the right and the third to the left, from underneath. Tuck the centre strand (A) under a strand of the standing part at the point at which the splice is required to start.

(b) Take the third strand (B), pass it over the strand under which the first tuck has just been made and tuck it under the next strand round. Always work from right to left.

(c) Turn the work over and tuck the remaining strand (C) under the one strand of the standing part now showing, working from right to left. Watch this move carefully as it is the most likely place for an error to occur. The usual mistake is to make the tuck from left to right as this seems to be the natural way.

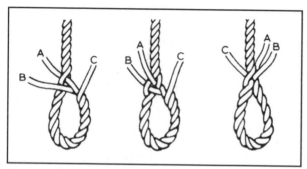

Fig 9.2 The eye splice.

If all is well, you should now have a strand of fibre radiating equally from each 'crack' in a section of the standing part. All that now remains is to take each strand in turn, starting with anyone, pass it over the strand in front of it and under the next one, pulling tight each time. Carry on until you run out of rope. In natural fibre rope a minimum of three tucks is required for reliability but with synthetic fibre rope at least five should be made. It is important to remember that these are *absolute minimum* figures; no marks will be lost for making many more but something vital like your mast, or even a life may be lost if fewer tucks are made.

To finish off, when there is insufficient strand left to make another tuck, trim the strands to within about ¼-inch of the rope with a hot soldering iron. Do not trim off too close or the tuck may pull out. Roll the splice under foot or between the palms of the hands to even out the tucks.

To make the tucks, the rope can be opened up by holding in the left hand and turning clockwise with the right. If the turns are too tight, an opening can be forced by inserting a blunt, tapered spike - a pencil makes a good substitute for the professional *lignum vitae fid*.

A hard eye is formed in exactly the same way except that the loop is formed round a thimble and the first tuck made as close to the thimble as possible. Work is made easier if the rope is temporarily seized to the thimble with light twine until the splice is finished.

MASTS

Apart from the conventional flagpole, a wide variety of ideas has been successfully tried by ingenious amateurs. A lot depends on what can be obtained locally in view of the transport difficulties, and also whether the mast is to support a wire or beam, or is to be used as the radiator itself. Excellent masts have been made from builder's scaffold poles (especially the dural variety), lengths of galvanised gas or water pipe screwed together, and even empty oil or beer cans soldered together. The new plastic fall-pipes can also be stacked to make good mast radiators by taping four lengths of copper wire to the outside. *The ARRL Handbook* contains several excellent suggestions for masts constructed from lengths of timber. However, whatever form the mast takes, unless it is of the self-supporting Eiffel Tower variety, the principles and practice of staying it remain the same.

Halyards

For most applications the ¾-inch circumference (¼-inch, 6mm, diameter) size Terylene or polypropylene will be ample; only a really large or heavy array will require anything stronger. To prevent premature fracture due to movement in the wind, a wire antenna should be kept under constant tension. One method is to hang a weight on the lower end of the halyard, taking care to lash it loosely to the mast to prevent it blowing about. On professional installations a short weighted lever is usually fixed to the base of the mast. For amateurs it is easier and cheaper to incorporate a small spring close to the insulator at the far end. The type of spring used to tension small boat steering wires is ideal; they are made of galvanised or stainless steel and cleverly arranged so the spring is actually under compressions and virtually unbreakable.

Perhaps the best way of all is to borrow a marine radio telephone technique and fit a neoprene insulator. This is a 24in (0.7 metre) length of synthetic rubber bar with a hard eye at each end and performs the dual purpose of insulating the antenna and providing tension. The halyard should be spliced through the first splice. This ensures that the halyard and insulator can be recovered should the antenna break. It also obviates the necessity of stowing a great heap of rope when the antenna is in position. For a really superior job, the main halyard splice should be finished off with a wall-and-crown knot. This puts a decorative knob at the end of the splice which prevents any tendency for the splice to be pulled into the pulley and jamming it. If the halyard lies close to the mast wind will slap it against the mast at frequent, regular intervals causing chafe and driving your neighbours to distraction. This can be prevented by positioning the pulley a foot or two away from the top of the mast or by giving the halyard two or three turns round the mast after the antenna has been raised.

If a tree is being used, some form of automatic tensioning device becomes vital. As the pulley cannot be shackled directly to a tree it must be shackled to the hard eye at the end of a length of rope, which is then tied to the tree with a round turn and two half-hitches if the strain is at right-angles, or a rolling hitch if it is not.

Guys

Non-rotting, non-stretching, non-shrinking, non-RF-absorbing Terylene or polypropylene makes excellent guys for radio masts. For light masts such as the 10m or 30ft by 1in ex-army jobs, the ¾-inch circumference (1/4-inch, 6mm, diameter) size with a breaking load of 1200lb will probably suffice, but for anything heavier, or in case of doubt, the 1in circumference (5/16-in, 8mm, diameter) size is preferred. This latter size offers an 80% increase in strength for only a 50% increase in cost and is well worth the little extra to sleep peacefully through the winter storms instead of having nightmares about the neighbour's greenhouse. Bear in mind that it is normally accepted that the maximum working load of a fibre rope should not exceed one sixth of its ultimate strength. In common with natural fibres, synthetics also suffer varying degrees of degradation from prolonged exposure to excessive ultra-violet radiation so it pays to err on the generous side regarding size and accept the increased strength as a bonus.

It is impossible to lay down any hard-and-fast rules regarding the number of sets of guys or the number of guys to a set as so much depends on the characteristics of the particular mast and the ground area available. As a rough guide, three guys to a set on a pitch circle diameter at least equal to the height of the mast is a good basis on which to start. A thin, flexible mast, such as the 10m (30ft) ex-army mast just mentioned, will require guying every 5m (15ft) or so, whereas a sturdy flag-pole may manage with one set at the top only. In theory only three guys per set are necessary but it may be more convenient to use four; a mast at the end of the average rectangular garden can then be anchored to the corners and down the sides.

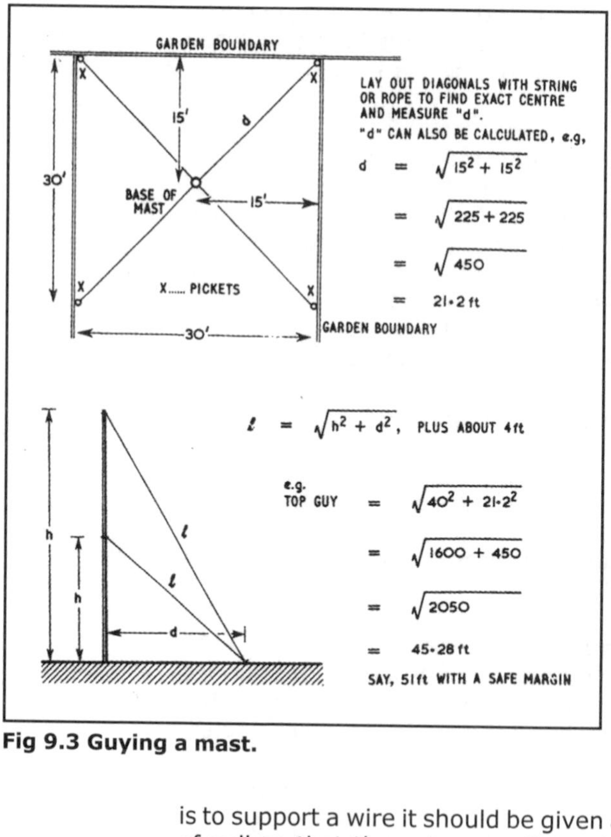

Guy lengths can be measured by drawing a scale diagram or calculated by courtesy of Pythagoras. As the guy forms the hypotenuse of a right-angled triangle, its length will be the square root of the sum of its height squared, plus the distance from the base squared (**Fig 9.3**). Then add three or four feet extra for splices, hitches etc.

Guys should not be set up too tightly; once the mast is being held in position any further tension simply puts the mast under compression, which tends to buckle it in the middle if it cannot be pushed into the ground. This is why high-stretch ropes like nylon and polythene are unsuitable. As a general rule the guys should look tight but not feel tight. If the mast is to support a wire it should be given a slight rake away from the direction of pull so that the antenna will tend to straighten it. This will obviously put a greater strain on the guys behind the mast, but it should not be possible to provide a musical accompaniment on them! If the mast is stiff enough to support itself without an antenna it should only be necessary to use two guys, spaced about 100° apart, at the top anyway, to balance

Fig 9.3 Guying a mast.

the pull of the antenna. If the pull is very strong it may be necessary to provide a second set at the middle to prevent buckling.

Pickets

Again, a lot depends on the size and weight of mast and antenna and the nature of the ground but, as a general guide, lengths of 50mm or 2in outside diameter galvanised pipe driven into the ground at an angle for two or three feet will make a good anchorage. The guy may then be tied directly to the picket using a round turn and two half-hitches, as the strain should be at a near right-angle. When all is settled the surplus rope should be bound to the guy to prevent any possibility of slip and to tidy the loose end. In soft ground it may be necessary to back up the picket with a similar one a foot or so behind, taking a stout lashing from the top of the first one to the bottom of the second.

Lengths of 50 x 50mm (2 x 2in) angle-iron also make excellent pickets. Unlike tube or rod, however, the guy cannot be tied directly to the angle-iron; in this case a hole must be drilled near the top and a shackle fitted. If 8mm (1in) circular are being used, the shackle should be fairly large - say, 3/8-inch or ½-inch.

The guy is then cut a little shorter than required and a hard eye spliced in. A lanyard comprising 2m (6ft) or so of 3/8 inch or 1/2 inch (3 or 4mm diameter) pre-stretched Terylene is then spliced to the eye and passed two or three times through the shackle and eye to form a simple tackle. To spread the load correctly and prevent chafe, the diameter of the shackle should at least equal the circumference of the lanyard. Three turns will roughly equal the strength of the guy, and the reduction ratio thus obtained will facilitate setting the tension exactly. This system may look rather crude but it was universally used for the rigging of sailing ships for several hundred years (and still is occasionally) and has proved to be extremely reliable as well as cheap.

Alternatively, if ¾-inch circular (6mm) guys are being used to support a light mast, the guy may be passed round a suitable thimble and a smaller shackle can be used. The loop should be formed with a rolling hitch; if this is tied correctly with the second turn jammed inside the first it should be possible to slide the knot up or down the guy to set the length, but the knot should not slide down by itself when left temporarily. When the correct setting has been obtained a seizing should be applied close to the thimble to prevent any possibility of slip.

Pickets can also be obtained in the form of a screw made from ¾-inch or 1in bar. Although not strong enough to be screwed into chalky or rocky ground, they are very easy to use in softer ground and are ideal for temporary installations.

ANTENNA CONSTRUCTION

Apart from the installation of masts, guys and ropes, careful consideration needs to be given to the construction of the antenna itself, and any metal parts that are made. In an article in the January 1989 *RadCom*, John Nelson, GW4FRX, described the effects of water on antennas and dissimilar metals.

A lot of antenna manufacturers do not yet seem to have tumbled to the fact that a) rain falls practically everywhere and b) there exists an interesting phenomenon known as electrolytic corrosion. The first point just means that you might have to do some thinking before you put the antenna up - can water get in the balun and can you stop it doing so, for example, or is it really satisfactory to have the inner of the feeder and two halves of a driven element appearing on three SO239 sockets mounted on a bracket on the boom and not protected from the weather? The second point is that the contact between dissimilar metals in an antenna system is likely to cause a lot of trouble. The reason is that every metal has its own 'electro-potential'. In fact, metals can be divided into two groups, known technically as 'anodic' and' cathodic'.

Into the 'anodic group' come the following:

Magnesium
Aluminium
Dural and most aluminium alloys
Zinc
Cadmium
Chromium iron alloys (ie some stainless steels)
Chromium nickel iron alloys (other stainless steels)
Tin-lead alloys (ie solder)
Tin

The following are 'cathodic':

Lead
Nickel
Brasses
Bronzes
Nickel-copper alloys (ie 'nichrome')
Copper
Silver alloys (ie silver solder)
Silver
Gold
Platinum

Condensing about 400 pages of physical chemistry into one sentence, if two dissimilar metals are put in contact, the difference in electro-potential will cause some corrosion at the point where they touch. This will be even worse when the joint gets wet. If two anodic, or two cathodic, metals are put together there will not be very much effect at all. However, putting a cathodic metal in contact with an anodic one will cause a lot of dismay after some time has passed. Cathodic metals corrode anodic ones; for example, if brass screws are used to assemble an antenna made of aluminium alloy, the aluminium will soon start to flake and crumble and ultimately it turns to a fine white powder whilst the brass sits there looking smug. As a matter of interest, the table above is given in order of electro-potential. Lead does not corrode tin very much but if a magnesium antenna is assembled with platinum screws (anyone ever seen platinum screws?) there would soon be big trouble.

If for some inconceivable reason it is necessary to use anodic and cathodic materials in close proximity on an antenna, make sure that water does not get in. Use copious quantities of 738 sealer as the best way to deal with the problem, although a better solution would be replacement of the offending hardware by something with the same electro-potential as whatever it is that is being assembled.

Antenna disassembly

It is also worth remembering that for maintenance and when it is necessary to remove an antenna it is necessary to take it apart. John Nelson, GW4FRX, also gives some ideas about this. Dismantling antennas and mountings is infinitely easier if some thought is given to this when they are being erected. Coating the brackets and bolts which hold the antenna to the mast with grease before assembling them, and spraying the insides of boom sections with WD40 or similar so that they come apart easily when the time comes all make a great difference. A bit of MS4 (or whatever silicon grease is to hand) on the element retaining clips helps enormously when the time comes to get them off the boom - a little bit of forethought and preparation can pay dividends later on, and it can even save having to scrap things which cannot be dismantled because they have seized solid and cannot therefore be removed from the mast.

Appendix

Wire size reference and conversion table

Wire Gauge Number	SWG inches	mm	AWG Inches	mm	Nearest metric reference to SWG
6	0.192	4.88	0.162	4.11	
7	0.176	4.47	0.144	3.66	
8	0.160	4.06	0.128	3.26	
9	0.144	3.66	0.114	2.90	
10	0.128	3.25	0.102	2.59	
11	0.116	2.95	0.091	2.30	
12	0.104	2.64	0.081	2.05	
13	0.092	2.34	0.072	1.83	
14	0.081	2.03	0.064	1.63	
15	0.072	1.83	0.057	1.45	
16	0.064	1.63	0.051	1.29	
17	0.056	1.42	0.045	1.15	1.5
18	0.048	1.22	0.040	1.02	1.25
19	0.040	1.02	0.036	0.91	1.00
20	0.036	0.92	0.032	0.81	
21	0.032	0.81	0.028	0.72	0.8
22	0.028	0.71	0.025	0.64	0.71
23	0.024	0.61	0.023	0.57	
24	0.023	0.56	0.020	0.51	0.56
25	0.020	0.51	0.018	0.45	0.5
26	0.018	0.46	0.016	0.40	
27	0.016	0.41	0.014	0.36	0.4
28	0.014	0.38	0.013	0.32	
29	0.013	0.35	0.011	0.29	
30	0.012	0.305	0.010	0.25	0.315

SWG = Standard Wire Gauge
AWG = American Wire Gauge
Diameters in millimetres have been derived from the original measurements in inches

Characteristics of radio frequency cables

(a) Coaxial RF Cables – British UniRadio Series

UR No.	Nominal Impedance Z_0 (ohms)	Overall diameter (inches)	Inner Conductor (inches)	Capacitance (pF/ft)	Maximum operating RMS voltage	Typical Attenuation dB / 100 Feet 10 MHz	100 MHz	Approx RG Equiv
43	52	0.195	0.032	29	2750	1.3	4.3	58/U
57	75	0.405	0.044	20.6	5000	0.6	1.9	11A/U
67	50	0.405	7/0.029	30	4800	0.6	2.0	213U
70	75	0.228	7/0.0075	20.5	6270	1.5	4.9	
76	51	0.195	19/0.0066	29	1800	1.6	5.3	58C/U
90	75	0.242	0.022	20	2500	1.1	3.5	59B/U
95	50	0.09	0.0018	30	900	2.6	8.2	174A/U
Above cables have solid dielectric and a velocity factor of 0.66								
202	75	0.20	7/0.0098	17		1.2	3.4	TV down lead
203	75	0.285	0.044	17		0.084	2.3	Low loss TV
Two above cables have a cellular polythene dielectric								

(b) Coaxial RF Cables – USA RG Series

RG No.	Nominal Impedance Z_0 (ohms)	Cable diameter (inches)	Velocity Factor	Typical Approx Attenuation dB / 100 Feet 10MHz	100MHz	Capacitance (pF/ft)	Maximum operating RMS
RG-8A/U	50.5	0.405	0.66	0.55	2.0	30.5	4000
RG-11A/U	75	0.405	0.66	0.7	2.3	20.5	5000
RG-58/U	53.5	0.195	0.66	1.25	4.65	28.5	1900
RG-59A/U	75	0.242	0.66	1.1	3.4	20.5	2300
RG-62A/U	93	0.242	0.84	0.85	2.7	13.5	750
RG-174A/U	50	0.11	0.66	3.4	10.6	30.3	1000
RG-213/U	50	0.405	0.66	0.6	1.9	29.5	5000

(C) Ribbon / flat RF cables

Type of Cable	Nominal Impedance Z_0 (ohms)	Dimensions (inches) Each conductor	Overall	Capacitance (pF/ft)	Approx Velocity Factor	Typical Approx Attenuation dB / 100 Ft 50 MHz	100 MHz
Flat twin (Permanoid 302)	80	0.036	0.16 x 0.10	20	0.7	2.9	5.1
Flat twin (Permanoid 306B)	300	14/0.0076	0.4 x 0.08	4.5	0.85	1.0	1.9
Slotted twin (Bofa GMP6)	300	7/0.012	0.4 x 0.11	3.36	0.9	0.64	1.4

Wire and coils

Coil inductance calculations can be difficult to undertake and as there are many variables, they may not be particularly accurate. As a guide to the approximate levels of inductance, the table below provides values that might be expected for air cored coils that might be used in antenna applications.

Winding details for four values of inductance

Inductance (µH)	Wire (SWG)	Diameter (in.)	Length (in.)	Number of turns
40	18	2.5	2	28
40	14	2.5	4.25	34
20	18	2.5	1.25	17
20	14	2.5	2.75	22
8.6	16	2	2	16
8.6	14	2.5	3	15
4.5	16	2	1.25	10
4.5	14	2.5	4	12

Index